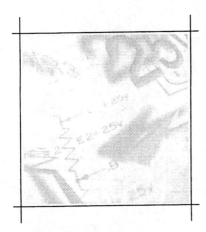

Solutions Manual

to Accompany

D1541160

MATHEMATICS FOR ELECTRICITY AND ELECTRONICS

SECOND EDITION

Arthur D. Kramer

DELMAR

THOMSON LEARNING™

Australia   Canada   Mexico   Singapore   Spain   United Kingdom   United States

DELMAR
™
THOMSON LEARNING

Solutions Manual to Accompany *Mathematics for Electricity & Electronics, 2nd edition*
by Arthur D. Kramer

Business Unit Director:
Alar Elken

Executive Editor:
Sandy Clark

Senior Acquisitions Editor:
Gregory L. Clayton

Development Editor:
Jennifer A. Thompson

Executive Marketing Manager:
Maura Theriault

Marketing Coordinator:
Karen Smith

Executive Production Manager:
Mary Ellen Black

Production Manager:
Larry Main

Senior Project Editor:
Christopher Chien

Art/Design Coordinator:
David Arsenault

For permission to use material from this text or product, contact us by
Tel (800) 730-2214
Fax (800) 730-2215
www.thomsonrights.com

Library of Congress Cataloging-in-Publication Data: 2001032534

ISBN 076682702X

NOTICE TO THE READER

Contents

Detailed solutions are shown for more difficult problems. For a group of identical problems, procedures are shown for the first one in the group and for any others that differ significantly.

CHAPTER 1   Basic Arithmetic

Exercise 1.1   Arithmetic Operations

1. 16
2. 15
3. 120
4. 160
5. 4
6. 57
7. 36
8. 7
9. 40
10. 5
11. 50
12. 2
13. 26

14. 14
15. 77
16. 9
17. 45
18. 200
19. 2
20. 30
21. 120
22. 40
23. 5
24. 5
25. 25

26. 9
27. 10
28. 19
29. 55
30. 150
31. 1500
32. 510
33. 1
34. 5
35. $\dfrac{180}{90} = 20$ mi/gal;

$\dfrac{210}{10} = 21$ mi/gal

36. tech $\dfrac{\$640}{40} = \$16$/hr;

teacher $\dfrac{\$570}{30} = \$19$/hr

37. $(6000)(9000)$
$= 54,000,000$ mi

38. $\dfrac{44 \text{ km}}{2 \text{ h}} = 22$ km/h

39. 1 A
40. 2 A
41. 16 V
42. 12 V
43. 7
44. 122

Exercise 1.2   Multiplying and Dividing Fractions

1. $\dfrac{3}{5}$
2. $\dfrac{1}{3}$
3. $\dfrac{4}{5}$
4. $\dfrac{1}{2}$
5. $\dfrac{3}{4}$
6. $\dfrac{2}{3}$
7. $\dfrac{2}{9}$
8. $\dfrac{3}{7}$
9. $\dfrac{2}{11}$
10. $\dfrac{6}{13}$
11. $\dfrac{2}{15}$
12. $\dfrac{1}{24}$

13. $\dfrac{4}{15}$
14. $\dfrac{11}{60}$
15. $\dfrac{4}{3}$
16. 6
17. $\dfrac{28}{45}$
18. $\dfrac{10}{11}$
19. 2
20. $\dfrac{1}{45}$
21. $\dfrac{5}{16}$
22. $\dfrac{11}{12}$
23. $\dfrac{5}{6}$
24. $\dfrac{5}{21}$

25. $\dfrac{2}{21}$
26. $\dfrac{1}{8}$
27. 6
28. 3
29. $\dfrac{1}{3}$
30. $\dfrac{1}{5}$
31. $\dfrac{1}{2}$
32. $\dfrac{2}{5}$
33. 8
34. $\dfrac{5}{14}$
35. $\dfrac{15}{50} = \dfrac{3}{10}$ ft

36. $\dfrac{3}{4}(100) = 75$ ft
37. $(1000)\left(\dfrac{3}{5}\right)\left(\dfrac{1}{2}\right) = \$300$
38. $(40,000)\left(\dfrac{1}{2}\right)\left(\dfrac{1}{4}\right) = \$5000$
39. 27 V
40. 60 V
41. $\dfrac{1}{16}$ A
42. $\dfrac{1}{50}$ A
43. $\dfrac{9}{25}$ W
44. $\dfrac{1}{20}$ W

Exercise 1.3   Adding Fractions

1. $\frac{7}{7} = 1$

2. $\frac{4}{5}$

3. $\frac{5}{8}$

4. $\frac{5}{6}$

5. $\frac{13}{20}$

6. $\frac{11}{14}$

7. $\frac{19}{24}$

8. $\frac{11}{12}$

9. $\frac{14}{15}$

10. $\frac{31}{60}$

11. $\frac{57}{200}$

12. $\frac{41}{75}$

13. $\frac{1}{4}$

14. $\frac{1}{10}$

15. $\frac{1}{6}$

16. $\frac{1}{60}$

17. $\frac{11}{20}$

18. $\frac{1}{20}$

19. $\frac{85}{24}$

20. $\frac{69}{35}$

21. 5

22. $\frac{3}{4}$

23. $\frac{33}{80}$

24. $\frac{37}{100}$

25. $\frac{127}{200}$

26. $\frac{49}{120}$

27. $\frac{7}{20}$

28. $\frac{7}{100}$

29. $\frac{63}{100}$

30. $\frac{15}{4}$

31. $\frac{31}{60}$

32. $\frac{7}{24}$

33. $\frac{2}{3}$

34. $\frac{5}{6}$

35. $\frac{7}{12}$

36. $\frac{6}{25}$

37. $\frac{1}{80}$

38. $\frac{59}{100}$

39. $\frac{13}{12}$

40. $\frac{3}{20}$

41. $\frac{14}{15}$

42. $\frac{3}{8}$

43. $\frac{41}{100}$

44. $\frac{1}{50}$

45. $\frac{11}{20}$

46. $\frac{3}{4}$

47. $\frac{1}{4}$

48. $\frac{11}{5}$

49. 1 lb

50. up $\frac{5}{8}$ lb

51. $\frac{13}{4}$ in

52. $\left[(5 \text{ ft } 3 \text{ in}) - (6)\left(\frac{1}{2} \text{ in} \right) \right] \div 5 = 1 \text{ ft}$

53. 10 Ω

54. 25 Ω

55. 20 Ω

56. 300 Ω

57. $\frac{20}{3}$ Ω

58. $\frac{40}{3}$ Ω

59. $\left(\frac{1}{10} \right)\left[3 \div \left(\frac{1}{2} \right) \right]\left(\frac{20}{3} \right) = 4$

60. $\frac{\frac{7}{10}}{\frac{9}{10}}\left(\frac{9}{20} \right) = \frac{7}{20}$

Exercise 1.4   Hand Calculator Operations

1. 4

2. 197

3. 47

4. 1900

5. 130

6. 12

7. 412

8. 4

9. 2

10. 3

11. 147

12. 32

13. 60

14. 3

15. 1

16. 2

17. 1

18. 1

19. 4

20. 2

21. 710 (OIL)

22. 142857

23. 666.7 Ω

24. 57.1 Ω

Review Exercises

1. 22

2. 47

3. 12

4. 400

5. 27

6. 135

7. $\frac{15}{4}$

8. $\frac{1}{2}$

9. $\frac{3}{2}$

10. $\frac{2}{5}$

11. $\frac{15}{2}$

12. $\frac{1}{9}$

13. $\frac{5}{2}$

14. $\frac{4}{5}$

15. $\frac{11}{16}$

16. $\frac{1}{50}$

17. $\frac{1}{5}$

18. $\frac{17}{6}$

19. $\frac{7}{24}$

20. $\frac{13}{40}$

21. $\frac{5}{36}$

22. $\frac{27}{100}$

23. $\frac{8}{7}$

24. $\frac{7}{16}$

25. 200

26. 58

27. 147

28. 2

29. 2

30. 3

31. 25 mi/h

32. $160

33. $\left(\dfrac{1}{2}\right)(500) = 250$ ft

34. $500 - 400 - 25 = \$75$

35. $1000 + 250 = \$1250$

36. $\left[7 - 15\left(\dfrac{4}{5}\right) \div 12\right] \div 16 = \dfrac{3}{8}$ ft

37. $\dfrac{1}{2}$ A

38. $\dfrac{1}{16}$ A

39. 10 V

40. $\dfrac{24}{5}$ V

41. $\dfrac{18}{5}$ W

42. 24 W

43. 27 V

44. $\dfrac{2}{5}$ A

45. 20 Ω

46. 60 Ω

47. 20 Ω

48. 37 Ω

49. $\dfrac{1}{5}\left(5 \div \dfrac{3}{5}\right)\left(\dfrac{5}{3}\right) = \dfrac{25}{9}$

50. $\dfrac{\left(\frac{7}{20}\right)\left(\frac{1}{2}\right)}{\frac{9}{10}} = \dfrac{7}{36}$

CHAPTER 2   Decimals and Percentages

Exercise 2.1   Decimals

1. 10.09

2. 65.129

3. 0.91

4. 69.384

5. 4.05

6. 1.202

7. 0.0062

8. 10.01

9. 12

10. 0.069

11. 6.25

12. 0.02804

13. 30

14. 210

15. 0.12

16. 33.01

17. 0.08

18. 2.8

19. 0.8

20. 1.612

21. 12.3

22. 0.87

23. 0.02

24. 0.15

25. 4

26. 0.121

27. 40

28. 0.55

29. 7

30. 0.3

31. 0.08

32. 0.4

33. 0.2083 mm

34. 3.12 cm

35. 0.5555 cm^2

36. 0.08 in, 0.0004 in^2

37. 40.10 V

38. 1.50 A

39. 17 cm

40. 4.4 mm, 1.21 mm^2

Exercise 2.2   Percentages

1. 0.75, 75%

2. 0.5, 50%

3. 0.4, 40%

4. 0.3, 30%

5. 15%, $\dfrac{3}{20}$

6. 25%, $\dfrac{1}{4}$

7. 10%, $\dfrac{1}{10}$

8. 60%, $\dfrac{3}{5}$

9. $\dfrac{1}{5}$, 0.2

10. $\dfrac{4}{5}$, 0.8

11. $\dfrac{43}{50}$, 0.86

12. $\dfrac{11}{20}$, 0.55

13. 0.05, 5%

14. 0.12, 12%

15. 1.25, 125%

16. 2.4, 240%

17. $\dfrac{1}{20}$, 5%

18. $\dfrac{2}{25}$, 8%

19. $\dfrac{3}{2}$, 150%

20. $\dfrac{1}{1}$, 100%

21. $\frac{6}{5}$, 1.2

22. $\frac{2}{1}$, 2.0

23. $\frac{7}{125}$, 0.056

24. $\frac{101}{200}$, 0.505

25. 33%, 0.33

26. 0.875, 87.5%

27. $\frac{3}{8}$, 37.5%

28. $\frac{1}{8}$, 12.5%

29. $\frac{17}{200}$, 0.085

30. $\frac{1}{16}$, 0.0625

31. $\frac{1}{1000}$, 0.1%

32. 0.002, 0.2%

33. 3

34. 16

35. 15

36. 30

37. 1.35

38. 1.19

39. 75

40. 12.5

41. 1.65

42. 0.4825

43. $13.20

44. $150.00

45. 0.95 ft^3

46. 30 g

47. $38.00, $42.75

48. $44.00

49. $64.00, $68.80

50. $20.00, $21.65

51. $42.00, $44.10

52. $642

53. 110%, $\frac{1120}{1000}$, $\frac{9}{8}$, $1\frac{1}{6}$, 1.19

54. 0.03, $\frac{1}{40}$, $\frac{0.5}{25}$, 0.50%

55. 165 Ω

56. 532 Ω

57. 0.11 A, 1.21 A

58. 0.22 A, 0.88 A

59. 40% decrease

60. 50% increase

61. 20% increase

62. 25% decrease

Exercise 2.3   Precision and Accuracy

1. 3

2. 3

3. 2

4. 2

5. 3

6. 4

7. 3

8. 2

9. 4

10. 1

11. 4

12. 5

13. 5

14. 1

15. 4

16. 3

17. 5, 5.2, 5.15

18. 3, 3.1, 3.10

19. 30, 31, 31.3

20. 0.4, 0.44, 0.445

21. 400,000, 380,000, 382,000

22. 100, 100, 101

23. 30, 29, 29.0

24. 20, 19, 18.9

25. 0.4, 0.44, 0.440

26. 10,000, 11,000, 10,700

27. 20, 20, 20.0

28. 40, 39, 39.1

29. 0.06, 0.056, 0.0556

30. 0.009, 0.0090, 0.00899

31. 700, 680, 678

32. 6000, 5800, 5830

33. 461 m^2

34. 5,570,000 m^3

35. 152 lb

36. 27.1 ft/s, 18.5 mi/h

37. 18 V

38. 3.0 A

39. 203 in^2

40. 0.046 cm^3

41. 120 V

42. 0.11 A

43. 1480 W

44. (a) 1.3 Ω
    (b) 1.28 Ω

45. (a) $43
    (b) $46

46. (a) $170
    (b) $172

Exercise 2.4   Hand Calculator Operations

1. 2

2. 8280

3. 21.1

4. 950

5. 2.0

6. 3

7. 0.5

8. 2.5

9. 147

10. 48.4

11. 2.4

12. 0.20

13. 0.68

14. 0.00844

15. 0.143

16. 0.75

17. 0.860

18. 2.69

19. 35.5

20. 124

21. 1.90

22. 167,000

23. 110

24. 505

25. 8.27

26. 0.0270

27. 0.00482

28. 0.000900

29. 0.00266

30. 20.7

31. 197,000,000 mi^2

32. 14.9 cm

33. (a) 4.67%
    (b) 19.1%

34. (76,200)(0.062) = $4724.40

35. 33.0 V

36. 295 V

37. 0.415 A

38. 0.338 A

Review Exercises

1. 31.26

2. 0.0011

3. 4.04

4. 220.1

5. 0.006

6. 0.144

7. 20

8. 0.025

9. 44

10. 0.01

11. 0.8, 80%

12. 0.125, 12.5%

13. 0.15, 15%

14. $\frac{3}{10}$, 30%

15. $\frac{4}{25}$, 16%

16. 2, 200%

17. $\frac{7}{20}$, 0.35

18. $\frac{1}{8}$, 0.125

19. $\frac{11}{200}$, 0.055

20. $\frac{9}{1000}$, 0.9%

21. 8.4

22. 24.5

23. 39

24. 0.9

25. 82.5

26. 8.55

27. 33

28. 3.4

29. 0.95

30. 0.058

31. 31.0

32. 0.867

33. 66.9

34. 149

35. 25.3 in, 26.7 in^2

36. $1317.50, $1240.00

37. $(40,000)(0.4)\left(\frac{3}{4}\right) = \$12,000$

38. $(317)(10)(0.75) = 2380$ Btu/h

39. $59.84, $64.33

40. $110

41. 76

42. 0.0048 s

43. (a) 0.41 A
   (b) 2.5 A

44. 210 Ω

45. 10%

46. 33%

47. $(4700)\left(\frac{1}{3}\right)(0.75) = 1175 \approx 1200$ Ω

48. 0.41 A

49. 21 mA

50. (a) $\frac{5}{15}(100\%) = 33\%$
   (b) $25\left(\frac{2}{3}\right) = 1.67 \approx 1.7$ Ω

CHAPTER 3 Powers of Numbers

Exercise 3.1 Powers

1. 81

2. 64

3. 128

4. 125

5. 100,000

6. 625

7. $\frac{1}{16}$, 0.0625

8. $\frac{27}{1000}$, 0.027

9. $\frac{9}{25}$, 0.36

10. $\frac{1}{125}$, 0.008

11. $\frac{1}{10,000}$, 0.0001

12. $\frac{49}{100}$, 0.49

13. 0.49, $\frac{49}{100}$

14. $\frac{36}{25}$, 1.44

15. $\frac{8}{125}$, 0.064

16. $\frac{1}{8}$, 0.125

17. 0.0001, $\frac{1}{10,000}$

18. $\frac{1}{625}$, 0.0016

19. $\frac{1}{9}$, 0.111 …

20. 50

21. 1

22. $\frac{7}{5}$, 1.4

23. $\frac{6}{125}$, 0.048

24. $\frac{1}{4}$, 0.25

25. $\frac{1}{8}$, 0.125

26. $\frac{67}{1000}$, 0.067

27. $\frac{1}{20}$, 0.05

28. $\frac{11}{100}$, 0.11

29. $\frac{9}{50}$, 0.18

30. $\frac{1}{500}$, 0.002

31. $\frac{5}{16}$, 0.3125

32. $\frac{3}{125}$, 0.024

33. $\frac{17}{250}$, 0.068

34. $\frac{21}{20}$, 1.05

35. $\frac{1}{9}$, 0.111 …

36. $\frac{1}{16}$, 0.0625

37. 0.512 cm^3

38. 8100 ft^2

39. $26,620

40. $140.26

41. 2.25 mm^2

42. 0.396 ft^3

43. 20 Ω

44. 125 Ω

45. 17 W

46. 50.7 W

47. 0.06 W

48. 18 W

Exercise 3.2 Powers of Ten

1. 10^3

2. 10^6

3. 10^0

4. 10^9

5. 10^{-6}

6. 10^{-3}

7. 10^{-4}

8. 10^{-1}

9. 10^{-2}

10. 10^{-5}

11. 100,000

12. 100,000,000

13. 1,000,000

14. 1

15. 0.01, $\frac{1}{100}$

16. 0.0001, $\frac{1}{10,000}$

17. 0.1, $\frac{1}{10}$

18. 0.001, $\frac{1}{1000}$

19. 0.000001, $\frac{1}{1,000,000}$

20. 0.000000001, $\frac{1}{1,000,000,000}$

21. 10^6

22. 10^9

23. 10^{-5}

24. 10^{-10}

25. 10^{-6}

26. 10^{-1}

27. 10^9

28. 10^6

29. 10^3

30. 10^4

31. 10^{-2}

32. 10^{-5}

33. $10^1 = 10$

34. 10^2

35. 10^{-2}

36. 10^{-6}

37. 10^{-1}

38. 10^{-4}

39. 10^4

40. 10^7

41. 10^2

42. $10^0 = 1$

43. 10^9

44. 10^{-6}

45. 10^{-1}

46. 10^{-8}

47. 12×10^2

48. $49 \times 10^0 = 49$

49. $24 \times 10^1 = 24 \times 10$

50. 72×10^2

51. 6×10^{-12}

52. 45×10^{-4}

53. 12×10^{-1}

54. 4×10^6

55. 3×10^3

56. 5×10^{-3}

57. 2.5×10^{-2}

58. 4.5×10^5

59. 0.75×10^6

60. 1×10^5

61. 16×10^3, 16,000

62. 40×10^{-6}, 0.000040

63. 7×10^{-9}, 0.000000007

64. 5×10^{12}, 5,000,000,000,000

65. 6.5×10^4, 65×10^3, 65,000

66. $6 \times 10^3 = 60 \times 10^2 = 6000$

67. $29 \times 10^{-4} = 2.9 \times 10^{-3}$, 0.0029

68. $43 \times 10^{-2} = 4.3 \times 10^{-1}$, 0.43

69. 480 W

70. 3.8 W

71. 3.0 V

72. 0.0099 V

73. 0.05 A

74. 0.11 A

75. 2000 Ω

76. 300,000 Ω

Exercise 3.3 Square Roots and Cube Roots

1. 4
2. 11
3. $\frac{5}{2}$
4. $\frac{3}{10}$
5. $\frac{2}{3}$
6. $\frac{2}{9}$
7. 0.8
8. 0.6
9. 0.1
10. 1.5
11. 0.09
12. 0.12
13. 3
14. 5
15. $\frac{1}{2}$
16. $\frac{2}{5}$
17. 0.1
18. 0.2
19. 10
20. 0.1
21. 28
22. 24
23. 1.4
24. 2.2
25. 12
26. 18
27. $0.6 = \frac{3}{5}$
28. $0.04 = \frac{1}{25}$
29. 2
30. $\frac{1}{5} = 0.2$
31. $0.1 = \frac{1}{10}$
32. $\frac{1}{2} = 0.5$
33. 64×10^9
34. 36×10^4
35. 16×10^8
36. 27×10^{12}
37. 0.64×10^{10}
38. 0.01×10^2
39. 9×10^{11}
40. 32×10^{10}
41. 4×10^3
42. 5×10^2
43. 12×10
44. 7×10^6
45. 0.5×10^2
46. 0.8×10^3
47. 2×10^3
48. 3×10
49. 6×10^3
50. 5×10^4
51. 0.2×10^1
52. 0.5×10^{-1}
53. 1.5×10^{-5}
54. 0.32×10^{-2}
55. 0.75×10^5
56. 4×10^2
57. 70 ft
58. 100 mm, 10 cm
59. 2.5
60. 0.1 ft
61. 20 Ω
62. 25 Ω
63. 60 V
64. 0.02 A
65. 0.2 A
66. 48 V
67. 6.4 W
68. 7.2 W
69. 0.05 A
70. 400 V
71. $\frac{16}{9} + \frac{2}{9} = 2$
72. $4(9) - 11 = 25$

Exercise 3.4 Hand Calculator Operations

1. 58.1
2. 0.885
3. 0.0101
4. 56.6
5. 0.655
6. 0.0364
7. 79.7
8. 8.95
9. 0.242
10. 2.95
11. 57.0
12. 0.202
13. 15.0
14. 0.940
15. 10.1
16. 0.606
17. 57.4
18. 2.19
19. 97.9
20. 2.74
21. 148 cm³
22. 341 m/s
23. 0.794 W
24. 4830 Ω

Review Exercises

1. 343
2. 121
3. $\frac{1}{16}$, 0.0625
4. $\frac{8}{125}$, 0.064
5. 0.216, $\frac{27}{125}$
6. 0.064, $\frac{8}{125}$
7. 0.01, $\frac{1}{100}$
8. 0.625, $\frac{5}{8}$
9. $\frac{2}{5}$, 0.4
10. $\frac{1}{250}$, 0.004
11. 0.29, $\frac{29}{100}$
12. 0.0625, $\frac{1}{16}$
13. 7
14. $\frac{6}{5}$, 1.2
15. $\frac{2}{5}$, 0.4
16. 2
17. 0.3, $\frac{3}{10}$
18. 0.11, $\frac{11}{100}$
19. 4
20. 0.3, $\frac{3}{10}$
21. 0.06, $\frac{3}{50}$
22. 0.9, $\frac{9}{10}$
23. 7
24. $\frac{7}{5}$, 1.4

25. 100,000,000

26. 0.00001, $\frac{1}{100,000}$

27. $\frac{1}{10,000}$, 0.0001

28. $10^3 = 1000$

29. $10^2 = 100$

30. $10^{-6} = 0.000001$, $\frac{1}{1,000,000}$

31. $10^4 = 10,000$

32. $10^{-4} = 0.0001$, $\frac{1}{10,000}$

33. $10^{-5} = 0.00001$, $\frac{1}{100,000}$

34. $10^{-1} = 0.1$, $\frac{1}{10}$

35. $10^6 = 1,000,000$

36. $10^{-6} = 0.000001$, $\frac{1}{1,000,000}$

37. 14×10^2

38. 24×10^{-8}

39. 2×10^{-3}

40. 4.5×10^{-1}

41. 0.11×10^{-9}

42. $2.5 \times 10^0 = 2.5$

43. 16×10^5

44. 1×10^{-6}

45. $6.5 \times 10^3 = 65 \times 10^2$

46. $12 \times 10^{-6} = 120 \times 10^{-7}$

47. 81×10^8

48. 6.75×10^6

49. 9×10^3

50. 0.6×10

51. 4×10^3

52. 0.2×10^2

53. 0.1×10^7

54. 0.8×10^2

55. 0.0140

56. 0.0301

57. 277

58. 0.308

59. 51.7

60. 0.136

61. 9.48

62. 0.326

63. 56 ft

64. $102.50

65. 50 mm = 5 cm

66. $0.216 \ \text{m}^3$

67. 50 Ω

68. 256 W

69. 0.04 A

70. $20 \times 10^2 = 2000$ Ω

71. 6.5 Ω

72. 22 V

73. $0.075 \times 10^3 = 75$ W

74. 0.013 A

75. 0.0031 Ω

76. 0.15

CHAPTER 4   Systems of Measurement

Exercise 4.1   Scientific and Engineering Notation

1. 4.26×10^{10}, 42.6×10^9

2. 1.17×10^7, 11.7×10^6

3. 9.30×10^{-4}, 930×10^{-6}

4. 3.01×10^{-5}, 30.1×10^{-6}

5. 2.35×10^0

6. 4.56×10^1, 45.6×10^0

7. 1.17×10^{-3}

8. 9.81×10^{-2}, 98.1×10^{-3}

9. 3.34×10^2, 334×10^0

10. 6.99×10^4, 69.9×10^3

11. 1.12×10^{-1}, 112×10^{-3}

12. 4.09×10^{-1}, 409×10^{-3}

13. 1.62×10^5, 162×10^3

14. 7.76×10^3

15. 5.64×10^7, 56.4×10^6

16. 3.36×10^2, 336×10^0

17. 1.14×10^{-7}, 114×10^{-9}

18. 3.45×10^{-2}, 34.5×10^{-3}

19. 5.28×10^1, 52.8×10^0

20. 3.84×10^{-1}, 384×10^{-3}

21. 5.69×10^{-3}

22. 1.560×10^0

23. 5.66×10^6

24. 8.91×10^{-2}, 89.1×10^{-3}

25. 26,400,000

26. 433,000

27. 0.00000390

28. 0.0000931

29. 1.45

30. 46.7

31. 112,000

32. 87,000

33. 0.0000105

34. 0.717

35. 871,000,000

36. 4,440,000

37. 1250

38. 0.0000101

39. 0.503

40. 0.0550

41. 9.42×10^{-3}

42. 3.67×10^3

43. 7.88×10^{12}

44. 4.43×10^{12}

45. 0.899×10^6

46. 744×10^3

47. 500×10^{-3}

48. 36.3×10^{-3}

49. 53.3×10^{-3}

50. 74.8×10^{-3}

51. 163×10^{-12}

52. 7.28×10^{-9}

53. 40.0×10^6

54. 4.88×10^0

55. 0.250×10^{12}

56. 21.4×10^{-6}

57. $\dfrac{1.85 \times 10^{13}}{5.3 \times 10^9} = \$3490.57$

58. $\dfrac{1.37 \times 10^{11}}{1.80 \times 10^{11}} = 76.0\%$

59. 2.40×10^{-6} m

60. 5.28×10^{11}

61. $\dfrac{(2 \times 10^6)(4.0 \times 10^9)(365)}{6.65 \times 10^6} = 439 \times 10^9$ kWh

62. $\dfrac{60}{130 \times 10^{-12}} = 462 \times 10^9$

63. 183×10^{-3} V

64. 36.9×10^{-3} W

65. 92.3×10^{-3} A

66. 106×10^{-6} A

67. $5.41 \times 10^3 \ \Omega$

68. 2.18 V

Exercise 4.2   Metric System (SI)

1. 2300 V

2. 560 W

3. 0.031 A

4. 0.33 Ω

5. 1500 Ω

6. 5200 mW

7. 1500 kV

8. 850 µA

9. 78 mC

10. 0.86 mA

11. 6800 kW

12. 85 mV

13. 7.4 MV

14. 6.0 MW

15. 1300 pF

16. 0.0012 mS

17. 3.9 MHz

18. 0.22 ms

19. 0.045 mH

20. 4.0 nF

21. 0.40 kg

22. 1.5 km

23. 0.23 mm

24. 0.087 g

25. 0.040 MV

26. 0.12 MΩ

27. 0.0034 A

28. 0.055 MW

29. 7500 mΩ

30. 560 µA

31. 880 pF

32. 680 µs

33. 4.1 m

34. 670 cm

35. 600 cm²

36. 0.55 cm²

37. 0.35 kHz

38. 0.076 µF

39. 5500 µs

40. 670 mA

41. 0.056 MΩ

42. 0.21 MV

43. $\dfrac{8600}{10^4} = 0.860$ m²

44. $10(100) = 1000 \text{ mm}^2$

45. 3.5 km

46. 0.004 mm

47. 0.56 ms, 560 μs

48. $(2 \times 10^{-5})(100) = 0.002 \text{ mm}^2$

49. 300 kV, 0.30 MV

50. 5400 kHz, 5,400,000 Hz

51. 1.3 V

52. 180 V

53. 0.16 A, 160 mA

54. 0.092 A, 92 mA

55. 0.48 MΩ, 480 kΩ

56. 460 Ω, 0.46 kΩ

57. 0.77 W, 770 mW

58. 24,000 W, 24 kW

59. 300 m, 30,000 cm

60. 720 kW, 0.72 MW

Exercise 4.3   The U.S. Customary System

1. 180 ft

2. 7.9 lb

3. 54 kg

4. 46 m

5. 1.3 hp

6. 11 J

7. 190 W

8. 16 J

9. 4.7 ft · lb

10. 250 ft²

11. 2600 J

12. 2.7 m²

13. 110 ft/s

14. 4.6 m/s

15. 40 cm

16. 2.1 in

17. $\frac{5}{9}(95 - 32) = 35°C$

18. $\frac{5}{9}(32 - 32) = 0°C$

19. 4900 ft

20. 25 cm

21. 160 hp

22. 9500 Btu

23. 250 g

24. 4.0 kW

25. 130 kg

26. 17 m/s

27. 0.055 in

28. (a) 443 m

(b) $\dfrac{4,400,000}{3.281^2} = 410,000 \text{ m}^2$

29. $\dfrac{(1.15)(5280)}{(3.281)(1000)} = 1.85 \text{ km}$

30. 100 kPa

31. $(98)(0.55) = 54 \text{ J} = (54)(0.7376) = 40 \text{ ft} \cdot \text{lb}$

32. $(1 \times 10^{-6})(3 \times 10^8)^2 = 9.0 \times 10^{10} \text{ J}$

33. $\dfrac{(1 \times 10^{-3})(100)}{0.3937} = 0.025 \text{ mm}$

34. (a) $\dfrac{2.06}{3.281} = 0.63 \text{ Ω/1000 ft}$

(b) $\dfrac{8.37}{1000^2}(3.281^2)(12^2) = 0.013 \text{ in}^2$

35. 13,000 hp

36. $4.3 \times 10^{-9} \text{ lb}_f$

37. $(1.1)(0.5) = 0.55 \text{ cm}^2 = (0.55)(0.3937^2) = 0.085 \text{ in}^2$

38. $\dfrac{1.93}{1.43 \times 10^2}(100^2) = 1.35 \text{ kW/m}^2$

Exercise 4.4   Hand Calculator Operations

1. 539

2. 60.5×10^3

3. 43.3×10^{12}

4. 575×10^3

5. 25×10^6

6. 3.16×10^9

7. 215×10^{-3}

8. 408

9. 430×10^6

10. 1.06×10^6

11. 2.08×10^6

12. 299×10^0

13. 1.24×10^{-3}

14. 2.89×10^6

15. 78.9 J

16. 6.46 cm

17. 4.20 V

18. 241 Ω

19. 747 Ω

20. 9.77 W

21. 30.3 kΩ

22. 184 kΩ

Review Exercises

1. 8.76×10^7, 87.6×10^6

2. 5.60×10^{-5}, 56×10^{-6}

3. 1.12×10^{-1}, 112×10^{-3}

4. 1.26×10^3

5. 3.47×10^5, 347×10^3

6. 5.67×10^0

7. 330,000,000

8. 0.00000555

9. 124

10. 971,000

11. 0.000339

12. 11,200,000

13. 0.594 W

14. 6500 kΩ

15. 45.3 µA

16. 5.67 MV

17. 0.670 nF

18. 56.0 µs

19. 56.0 cm

20. 59.3 cm

21. 32.0 kV

22. 230 mH

23. 26.5 lb

24. 394 ft

25. 0.762 ft

26. 2.61 kW

27. 7.11 hp

28. 2.76 ft

29. 4.47 MW

30. 22,100 ft · lb

31. 33.0×10^3

32. 42.3×10^{-3}

33. 91.3×10^{12}

34. 2.45×10^3

35. 200×10^{-6}

36. 422×10^6

37. 2.05×10^{-3}

38. 168×10^{-9}

39. 3.18

40. 21.8×10^9

41. 500×10^9

42. 24.0×10^3

43. 6,370 km = 6.37×10^3 km = 3960 mi = 3.960×10^3 mi

44. 9.10×10^{-25} mg = 910×10^{-27} mg
$= (910 \times 10^{-27})(0.002205) = 2.01 \times 10^{-30}$ lb

45. $(7.62)(0.1)(0.3937) = 0.300$ in $\rightarrow$ 30 caliber

46. $\dfrac{360}{13.30}\left[(3600)\dfrac{0.001}{3.281}\right] = 29.7$ km/h

47. 150,000 kW = 201×10^3 hp

48. 5.18×10^{11} gal = 518×10^9 gal

49. 1.47 kΩ = 1470 Ω

50. 2.67 MΩ = 2670 kΩ

51. 56.4 V

52. 0.677 W = 677 mW

53. 0.011 A = 11.0 mA

54. 487 Ω = 0.487 kΩ

55. 2220 Ω = 2.22 kΩ

56. 1.75 MΩ = 1750 kΩ

57. 8.33×10^{-3} H

58. 375 μH = 0.375 mH

59. 50.4×10^{-6} H = 50.4 μH

60. 303×10^{-6} H = 303 μH

CHAPTER 5   Basic Algebra

Exercise 5.1   Signed Numbers

1. −3

2. 4

3. −10

4. 7

5. 4

6. 0

7. 5

8. −13

9. 5.3

10. −0.70

11. 5

12. 3.8

13. $\frac{1}{6}$ (0.17)

14. $-\frac{1}{2}$ (−0.5)

15. $\frac{5}{8}$ (0.625)

16. $-\frac{1}{20}$ (−0.05)

17. −56

18. 72

19. 3

20. $-\frac{1}{21}$ (−0.048)

21. −7

22. 3

23. −2

24. −0.1

25. −75

26. −180

27. 0.06

28. $\frac{3}{2}$(1.5)

29. −2

30. $\frac{1}{5}$(0.2)

31. −0.11

32. 30

33. 0

34. 0

35. $-\frac{5}{2}$ (−2.5)

36. 1

37. −27

38. −0.6

39. 48

40. −3

41. $-\frac{1}{5}$ (−0.2)

42. 0

43. $-\frac{1}{2}$ (−0.5)

44. −5

45. $\frac{23}{6}$ (3.83)

46. $\frac{1}{2}$ (0.5)

47. $\frac{3}{2}$ (1.5)

48. $-\frac{1}{2}$ (−0.5)

49. −22

50. −1.1

51. 8848 m − (−11,034 m) = 19,882 m; 29,028 ft − (−36,201 ft) = 65,229 ft

52. −183.0 − (−218.4) = 35.4°C

53. 0° − 45° + 90° = + 45°

54. −8 yd + 14 yd − 5 yd = +1 yd

55. positive

56. negative

57. −158°C

58. −3.0 V

59. 1.3 + 0.8 − 1.7 − 0.4 = 0

60. 12.6 + 12.9 − 10.3 − 8.2 − 7.0 = 0

Exercise 5.2   Algebraic Terms

1. 451

2. 3.82

3. 390

4. 95.1

5. 1.33

6. 0.0362

7. 140

8. 2.33

9. 677

10. 221

11. $-2x$

12. $5f$

13. $11q - 4p$

14. $3y - 8x$

15. $2IR + 16V$

16. $P - 14VI$

17. $x^2 - 3x$

18. $2a^2b$

19. $-1.5V_1 - 2.3V_2$

20. $5.8C_1 - 5.6C_2$

21. $-\left(\dfrac{1}{2}\right)P - \dfrac{1}{20}$

22. $-\left(\dfrac{1}{10}\right)f + \dfrac{4}{5}$

23. $-by - 1$

24. $8pr + 10p$

25. $7V - I$

26. $C + F$

27. $5x^2 - x + 1$

28. $-5z^2 - 9z - 6$

29. $4h^2 + 5h + 5$

30. $5n^2 + 5n + 9$

31. $\dfrac{R_x}{3}$

32. $\dfrac{7I_1}{8} - \dfrac{I_2}{2}$

33. $-4.5P_2 + 8.9P_1$

34. $20C_1 - 2C_2$

35. $5\pi + 1$

36. $xy^2 + 2$

37. $5V_0 - 2V_1$

38. $-2I_T + 16$

39. $n^2 - 3n$

40. 1

41. $8H + 1$

42. $4 + 6a - 2b$

43. $1.3v - 1.1r$

44. $1.9e - 2.0i$

45. $3\pi rh - 2\pi r^2$

46. $\frac{1}{2}mv^2 - 1.92$

47. $7d^2 + d - 4$

48. $2.4e^2 + 13.6e + 1.4$

49. $3.8IR + 0.4$

50. $2.58I^2R + 17.56$

51. $\left(\dfrac{1}{3}W - 5\right) - \left(\dfrac{1}{4}W - 7\right) = \dfrac{1}{12}W + 2$

52. $2Q^4 + \left(\dfrac{1}{6}\right)Q^2$

Exercise 5.3   Rules for Exponents

1. x^7

2. z^4

3. -1

4. 16

5. y^9

6. $(0.1)^6 = 0.000001$

7. R^2

8. n^3

9. -6

10. $7^2 = 49$

11. v^6

12. P^9

13. $(-2)^6 = 64$

14. $5C^8$

15. $27p^3v^6$

16. $16c^8d^4$

17. 10^9

18. $\dfrac{1}{10^2} = 0.01$

19. $\dfrac{x^2}{9b^4}$

20. $\dfrac{0.001w^6}{p^3}$

21. I^2

22. I^2

23. a^6

24. 0.5

25. $\dfrac{1}{8^2} = \dfrac{1}{64}$

26. 1

27. $\dfrac{1}{(-3^3)} = -\dfrac{1}{27}$

28. $\dfrac{1}{(2^5)} = \dfrac{1}{32}$

29. 1

30. $\dfrac{1}{10} = 0.1$

31. $\dfrac{9}{2} = 4.5$

32. $\left(\dfrac{5}{3}\right)^2 = \dfrac{25}{9}$

33. $(-2)^3 = -8$

34. $\left(-\dfrac{4}{3}\right)^2 = \dfrac{16}{9}$

35. $9^2 = 81$

36. $10^3 = 1000$

37. I^2

38. p^2

39. $\dfrac{9}{T^2}$

40. $4\pi^3r^4$

41. $-\dfrac{v}{4}$

42. R^3

43. $10^3 = 1000$

44. $\dfrac{1}{10} = 0.1$

45. $0.006a^2b^2$

46. $-0.008R^4t^5$

47. $5m^3 - 5m^2 + 15m$

48. $-24s^3 - 9s^2 + 3$

49. $30y^3$

50. $0.2L$

51. $2a - b$

52. $-2k^2 + k - 3$

53. $3f - 2$

54. $C_1 + C_2^2$

55. $x^3y + xy^3$

56. $15u^3v^4 - 15u^4v^3$

57. $\left(\dfrac{1}{25}\right) \times 10^6 = 40 \times 10^3$

58. 16×10^{-12}

59. 4×10^3

60. 3×10^{-2}

61. 720×10^{-9}

62. 2.73×10^3

63. 2.03×10^{-3}

64. 379×10^0

65. 2.00×10^{-3}

66. 198×10^{-9}

67. 12.0 V

68. 43.7 mW

69. 3.63 mA

70. 3.30 kΩ

71. 43.7 mW

72. 43.6 mW

73. 3.63 mA

74. 12.0 V

75. 11 kΩ

76. 850 Ω

77. 120 Ω

78. 600 Ω

79. 1.74×10^{-3} Ω = 1.74 mΩ

80. 6.96×10^{-3} Ω = 6.96 mΩ

81. 982 kHz

82. 159 kHz

83. $2 * X\text{^}3 - 6 * X\text{^}2 + 10 * X$

84. $X\text{^}2 + 2 * X - 3$

Review Exercises

1. 2

2. −2.7

3. −8.1

4. 20

5. $-\frac{1}{8}$

6. $-\frac{1}{14}$

7. 7

8. −150

9. −0.6

10. −2

11. $\frac{3}{4}$

12. −10

13. $-\frac{4}{5}$

14. $-\frac{1}{3}$

15. −3.8

16. 50

17. $3x - 2x^2$

18. $4a^2b$

19. $0.4V_1 - 1.1V_2$

20. $\left(\frac{1}{10}\right)F - \left(\frac{2}{5}\right)G$

21. $-4 + 5CV$

22. $5V - IR$

23. $-\dfrac{R_x}{3}$

24. $2xy^2 + x^2y$

25. $5.5I_1 - 2.7$

26. $1.5g - 1.1f$

27. m^9

28. k^4P^4

29. $(-1)^9 = -1$

30. $6^2 = 36$

31. q^{12}

32. $(-4)^4 = 256$

33. $64x^6y^2$

34. 10^{12}

35. $\dfrac{1}{f^3}$

36. $\dfrac{0.001p^6}{w^3}$

37. 1

38. $\frac{1}{64}$

39. $\frac{3}{4}$

40. 5

41. $-21X_C^4$

42. 0.6×10^{-3}

43. $180I^5R^5$

44. $-42t^3 - 54t^2 + 6t$

45. $\dfrac{20x}{w}$

46. $P_1P_2 + 1$

47. $42a^3b^3 - 42a^2b^4$

48. $\dfrac{0.3}{H}$

49. 2.94×10^9

50. 225×10^6

51. $\left(\frac{4}{5}\right) \times 10^{-2} = 8 \times 10^{-3}$

52. $35 \times 10^0 = 35$

53. $250 - (-70.5) = 320.5°C$

54. +49°F

55. $-2.6e^2 + 12.6e + 0.2$

56. $\left(\frac{3}{8}\right)mv_1^2$

57. −3.0 V

58. $12.9 - 12.9 = 0$

59. **(a)** 48.5 mA
(b) 776 mW

60. **(a)** 424 Ω
(b) 7.07 kΩ

61. 12.0 Ω

62. 500 Ω = 0.50 kΩ

63. 6.45 kΩ

64. 8.50×10^{-3} N

65. 4.77 A

66. 1.05 kΩ

CHAPTER 6   Computer Number Systems

Exercise 6.1   Binary Number System

1. $1(1000) + 3(100) + 2(10) + 8(1)$
2. $5(1000) + 5(100) + 8(10) + 6(1)$
3. $9(10,000) + 9(1000) + 1(100) + 5(10) + 0(1)$
4. $4(10,000) + 5(1000) + 2(100) + 1(10) + 7(1)$
5. $3(10) + 8(1) + 9(0.1) + 6(0.01)$
6. $2(10) + 1(1) + 1(0.1) + 5(0.01) + 2(0.001)$
7. $1(10) + 0(1) + 0(0.1) + 1(0.01)$
8. $1(100) + 0(10) + 1(1) + 1(0.1) + 1(0.01)$
9. 3
10. 2
11. 4
12. 7
13. 14
14. 9
15. 17
16. 21
17. 51
18. 36
19. 2.75
20. 3.25
21. 1.625
22. 2.125
23. 3.6875
24. 1.9375
25. 100
26. 110
27. 1011
28. 11011
29. 111 001
30. 111 111
31. 1 100 011
32. 1 101 111
33. 10 000 000
34. 11 001 000
35. 0.1
36. 0.11
37. 0.111
38. 0.011
39. 10.01
40. 111.001
41. 100 001.101
42. 101.1001

43.

17	10	001	25	11	001
18	10	010	26	11	010
19	10	011	27	11	011
20	10	100	28	11	100
21	10	101	29	11	101
22	10	110	30	11	110
23	10	111	31	11	111
24	11	000	32	100	000

44. (a) $2^7 = 128, 2^6 = 64 \rightarrow 7$ digits
   (b) $2^{10} = 1024, 2^9 = 512 \rightarrow 10$ digits
   (c) $2^{14} = 16,384, 2^{13} = 8192 \rightarrow 14$ digits
   (d) $2^{20} = 1,048,576, 2^{19} = 524,288 \rightarrow 20$ digits

45. (a) 49   (c) 7
    (b) 40   (d) 12

46. $2(0.8) = 1.6, 2(0.6) = 1.2, 2(0.2) = 0.4,$
    $2(0.4) = 0.8 \ldots$ repeats $\rightarrow 0.8 = 0.1100\ 1100\ 1100 \ldots$

Exercise 6.2   Binary Arithmetic

1. 101
2. 111
3. 1011
4. 1110
5. 1111
6. 1010
7. 1000.1
8. 110.11
9. 1111
10. 10 010
11. 10011
12. 1110
13. 10 000.01
14. 10 010.10

15. (a)   78   (b)   78
          + 86   + 87
          ‾‾‾‾   ‾‾‾‾
          164 →   X̶65 = 65
          64 + 1 = 65

16. (a)   132   (b)   132
          + 43   + 44
          ‾‾‾‾   ‾‾‾‾
          175 →   X̶76 = 76
          75 + 1 = 76

17. (a)   1001   (b)   1001
          + 888   + 889
          ‾‾‾‾   ‾‾‾‾
          1889 →   X̶890 = 890
          889 + 1 = 890

18. (a)   999   (b)   999
          + 888   + 889
          ‾‾‾‾   ‾‾‾‾
          1887 →   X̶888 = 888
          887 + 1 = 888

19. (a)   111   (b)   111
          + 010   + 011
          ‾‾‾‾   ‾‾‾‾
          1001 →   X̶010 = 10
          001 + 1 = 10

20. (a)   1101   (b)   1101
          + 0101   + 0110
          ‾‾‾‾‾   ‾‾‾‾‾
          1010 →   X̶011 = 11
          010 + 1 = 11

21. (a)   1111   (b)   1111
          + 1001   + 010
          ‾‾‾‾‾   ‾‾‾‾
          11000 →   X̶1001 = 1001
          1000 + 1 = 1001

22. (a)   10110   (b)   10110
          + 11010   + 11011
          ‾‾‾‾‾‾   ‾‾‾‾‾‾
          110000 →   X̶100011 = 10001
          10000 + 1 = 10001

23.   110
          + 011
          ‾‾‾‾
          X̶001 = 1

24.   111
          + 010
          ‾‾‾‾
          X̶001 = 1

25.   1101
          + 0110
          ‾‾‾‾‾
          X̶0011 = 11

26.   1100
          + 1001
          ‾‾‾‾‾
          X̶0101 = 101

27.   11000
          + 11010
          ‾‾‾‾‾‾
          X̶10010 = 10010

28.   10111
          + 10001
          ‾‾‾‾‾‾
          X̶01000 = 1000

29.   100.01
          + 110.01
          ‾‾‾‾‾‾
          X̶010.10 = 10.10

30.   1110.1
          + 1010.1
          ‾‾‾‾‾‾
          X̶1001.0 = 1001.0

31.   10110
          + 10011
          ‾‾‾‾‾‾
          X̶01001 = 1001

32.   0000 110111
          + 1111 101100
          ‾‾‾‾‾‾‾‾‾‾‾
          10000100011 →
          100011 + 1 = 100100

Exercise 6.3   Octal Number System

1. 10

2. 15

3. 53

4. 56

5. 212

6. 413

7. 4095

8. 513

9. 11

10. 15

11. 46

12. 74

13. 324

14. 741

15. 2114

16. 5726

17. 1000

18. 1101

19. 10011

20. 11 100

21. 111 110 001

22. 101 010 000

23. 1 000 101 100

24. 100 000 111 110

25. 14

26. 13

27. 33

28. 27

29. 57

30. 50

31. 312

32. 164

33. (a) $110\ 010\ 011_2 = 403$
     (b) $245_8 = 165$

34. (a) $620_8 = 110\ 010\ 000_2$
     (b) $144_8 = 1\ 100\ 100_2$

35.

17	21	10001	25	31	11001
18	22	10010	26	32	11010
19	23	10011	27	33	11011
20	24	10100	28	34	11100
21	25	10101	29	35	11101
22	26	10110	30	36	11110
23	27	10111	31	37	11111
24	30	11000	32	40	100000

36. $61_8 = 49$

Exercise 6.4   Hexadecimal Number System

1. 27

2. 46

3. 160

4. 195

5. 205

6. 255

7. 291

8. 645

9. 2571

10. 3047

11. 16.125

12. 44.625

13. 4097

14. 65536

15. 15

16. 18

17. 28

18. 23

19. 55

20. 48

21. 8E

22. 74

23. 157

24. 1A5

25. 3E8

26. 3F2

27. 11 0010

28. 1000 1001

29. 1010 1011

30. 1111 1110

31. 110 1100 0111

32. 1011 1000 0001

33. 1 1110 0000 1011

34. 10 1010 0010 1010

35. 1100 0000 1101 0000

36. 1111 0001 0001 0001

37. E

38. B

39. 1B

40. 1D

41. 2F

42. 3F

43. 5C

44. 5A

45. E9

46. 80

47. $1010\ 0000_2 = 240_8 = A0_{16}$

48. $1\ 0101\ 0101_2 = 525_8 = 155_{16}$

49. $59A_{16} = 1434$

50. $DE6_{16} = 3558$

Exercise 6.5   Computer Codes

1. (a) 0001 1000
  (b) 10010

2. (a) 0011 0111
  (b) 100101

3. (a) 0001 0010 0010
  (b) 111 1010

4. (a) 0010 0101 0011
  (b) 1111 1101

5. (a) 0011 0100 1001
  (b) 1 0101 1101

6. (a) 0011 0101 0110
  (b) 1 0110 0100

7. (a) 0101 1000   0011 0111
  (b) 58 37
  (c) 88 55

8. (a) 0011 0011   0100 1101
  (b) 33 4D
  (c) 51 77

9. (a) 0100 0011   0100 1001
      0100 0001
  (b) 43 49 41
  (c) 67 73 65

10. (a) 0100 0110   0100 0010
       0100 1001
  (b) 46 42 49

  (c) 70 66 73

11. (a) 0101 0011   0100 0001
       0100 1101
  (b) 53 41 4D
  (c) 83 65 77

12. (a) 0100 0010   0100 1111
       0100 0010
  (b) 42 4F 42
  (c) 66 79 66

13. (a) 0101 0010   0100 1111
       0101 0011   0100 0101
  (b) 52 4F 53 45
  (c) 82 79 83 69

14. (a) 0100 1010 0100 1111
0101 0011 0100 0101

  (b) 4A 4F 53 45

  (c) 74 79 83 69

15. (a) Number of bits used to denote a character

  (b) 9 bits

16. (a) A set of bytes processed as a group

  (b) 64

17. 0 0100 1110 0 0101 1001
1 0100 0011

18. 0 0100 1100 1 0100 0001
0 0101 1000

19. 707

20. BIT

21. (a) 0010 0100

  (b) 24

22. 0 0100 1001, spells ASCII

23. The minus should be 0 0110 1111.

24. The number 3 should be 1 0011 0011.

Review Exercises

1. 15

2. 13

3. 27

4. 62

5. 4.75

6. 5.625

7. 10011

8. 100010

9. 101 1000

10. 111 1101

11. 0.11

12. 101.1

13. 1100

14. 1110

15. 10011

16. 101.01

17. Using 2's
complement: 1010
            + 011
            ̸1̸01 = 101

18. Using 2's
complement: 1100
            + 0111
            ̸1̸0011 = 11

19. Using 2's
complement: 10000
            + 0001
            ̸1̸0001 = 1

20. Using 2's
complement: 11001
            + 0010
            ̸1̸1011 = 1011

21. 61

22. 119

23. 58

24. 235

25. 378

26. 3501

27. 100 110

28. 100 0011

29. 10 1010

30. 1000 1011

31. 1001 1100 1101

32. 1111 1110 0101

33. (a) 33

  (b) 1B

34. (a) 77

  (b) 3F

35. (a) 157

  (b) 6F

36. (a) 533

  (b) 15B

37. (a) 2040

  (b) 420

38. (a) 4100

  (b) 840

39. (a) 7

  (b) 7

40. (a) 15

  (b) D

41. (a) 23

  (b) 13

42. (a) 36

  (b) 1E

43. (a) 125

  (b) 55

44. (a) 314

  (b) CC

45. 0100 0111 0100 1111

46. 0011 0001 0011 0000 0011 0001

47. 0101 1000 0101 0011 0011 0011

48. 0101 0011 0100 0101 0100 0001

49. (Haste makes) waste = 57 41 53 54 45

50. (L O V) E = 0100 0101

51. Equals should be: 1 0011 1101

52. (a) 1100 → 0100 → 1100

  (b) 101 1000 → 010 1000 → 101 1000

CHAPTER 7 First-Degree Equations

Exercise 7.1 Solution of First-Degree Equations

1. 4
2. −5
3. −8.6
4. 3.5
5. 52
6. 78
7. 55
8. 18
9. 5
10. 12
11. −1
12. 1

13. 16
14. 7
15. 0.5
16. −0.2
17. −11
18. −30
19. 3
20. −4
21. 1.5
22. 4.3
23. 8.0
24. 1

25. 0
26. 0
27. 1.6
28. 3
29. 5.5
30. 0.5
31. $\frac{2}{3} = 0.67$
32. $-\frac{1}{5} = -0.2$
33. 5
34. −4
35. 68

36. 115
37. 12
38. −2.5
39. −25°C
40. 71.6°F
41. 3.5 sec
42. 36 ft
43. 100 V
44. 1.3 A
45. 24 W
46. 210 W

Exercise 7.2 Equation Solving Methods

1. −4
2. −3
3. −6
4. 8
5. 6
6. 0.5
7. 2.3
8. −3
9. 6
10. 0
11. $\frac{1}{3} = 0.33$

12. $\frac{1}{2} = 0.5$
13. −2
14. −7
15. 1.5
16. 4.4
17. −1
18. −1
19. −2.3
20. 0.4
21. −8
22. $\frac{5}{6} = 0.83$

23. 3
24. −0.5
25. 12
26. 175
27. 24
28. −20
29. 4.8
30. 12
31. 0.8
32. 0.5
33. 17

34. 25
35. 2
36. −2
37. $24.80
38. $825
39. 500 V
40. 480
41. 15 V
42. 13.5 V
43. 33 Ω
44. 9.0 Ω

Review Exercises

1. 6
2. 6
3. 1.5
4. 16.5
5. −5
6. $\frac{1}{4} = 0.25$
7. $-\frac{3}{5} = -0.60$

8. $\frac{3}{2} = 1.5$
9. 2
10. $\frac{1}{3} = 0.33$
11. 2
12. 3
13. 50
14. 15

15. $\frac{1}{2} = 0.5$
16. $\frac{19}{2} = 9.5$
17. 100
18. −12
19. $-\frac{3}{4} = -0.75$
20. −0.2
21. 12 h, 9 h, 3 h

22. $1000
23. 21 V
24. 24 V
25. 7.5 Ω
26. 1.6 A

CHAPTER 8   Basics of DC Circuits

Exercise 8.1   DC Circuits and Ohm's Law

1. 3.3 A

2. 500 mA

3. 120 V

4. 38 V

5. 7.5 Ω

6. 120 Ω

7. 1.5 V

8. 45 V

9. 3.3 mA

10. 430 μA

11. 17 V

12. 2.6 V

13. 3.0 kΩ

14. 910 Ω

15. 2.2 mA

16. 820 μA

17. 24 kΩ

18. 5.5 kΩ

19. (a) 3.6 A

   (b) $\dfrac{3.6}{2} = 1.8$ A

   (c) 3.6(0.9) = 3.2 A

20. (a) 30 mA

   (b) 2(30) = 60 mA

   (c) 1.5(30) = 45 mA

21. (a) 160 mA

   (b) R increases to $\frac{4}{3}$ of its value,

     hence $I = \left(\dfrac{3}{4}\right)(160) = 120$ mA

   (c) R doubles, hence $I = \left(\dfrac{1}{2}\right)(160) = 80$ mA

22. (a) 50 mA

   (b) $\left(\dfrac{3}{2}\right)(50) = 75$ mA

   (c) 2(50) = 100 mA

23. (a) 2(2.8) = 5.6 A

   (b) 1.25(2.8) = 3.5 A

24. (a) $\left(\dfrac{1}{3}\right)(120) = 40$ mA

   (b) (0.50)(120) = 60 mA

25. (a) 3(50) = 150 mA

   (b) 2(50) = 100 mA

26. (a) $\left(\dfrac{1}{3}\right)(3.0) = 1.0$ A

   (b) $\left(\dfrac{1}{2}\right)(3.0) = 1.5$ A

27. (a) $\left(\dfrac{15}{10}\right)(40) = 60$ mΩ

   (b) (1.25)(40) = 50 mΩ

28. (a) $\left(\dfrac{6}{10}\right)(40) = 24$ mΩ

   (b) (0.75)(40) = 30 mΩ

29. (a) $\left(\dfrac{150}{300}\right)(100\%) \rightarrow V$ increases 50%

   (b) $\left(\dfrac{30}{300}\right)(100\%) \rightarrow V$ decreases 10%

30. (a) $\left(\dfrac{3}{3}\right)(100\%) \rightarrow I$ increases 100%

   (b) $\left(\dfrac{1.5}{3}\right)(100\%) \rightarrow I$ decreases 50%

31. (a) R increases $\frac{2}{1}$

   (b) I increases to $\frac{3}{2}$ its value $\rightarrow$ R decreases $\frac{2}{3}$

32. I decreases by 50% or $\frac{1}{2}$. Using Ohm's law, R increases by the reciprocal ratio as follows:

$$\frac{3\text{ V}}{20\text{ mA}} \div \frac{3\text{ V}}{40\text{ mA}} = \frac{150\ \Omega}{75\ \Omega} = \frac{2}{1}$$

Exercise 8.2   Electric Power

1. 5.5 W, 22 Ω

2. 180 W, 80 Ω

3. 1.5 A, 5.3 Ω

4. 650 mA, 15 Ω

5. 13 V, 8.9 Ω

6. 75 V, 380 Ω

7. 14 W, 1.2 A

8. 4.0 W, 200 mA

9. 6.4 W, 32 V

10. 11 W, 27 V

11. 10 Ω, 3.1 A

12. 8.1 Ω, 1.1 A

13. 22 Ω, 18 V

14. 390 Ω, 630 V

15. 2.0 A, 600 V

16. 550 mA, 11 V

17. 37 V, 670 mA

18. 18 V, 550 mA

19. 1.7 mW, 120 kΩ

20. 20 Ω, 73 mA

21. 3.0 W, 68 V

22. 19 mW, 27 mA

23. 160 Ω, 240 V

24. 24 Ω, 600 mV

25. 19 mA, 2.9 V

26. 29 V, 8.7 mA

27. 3.3 kW, 600 mA

28. 3.8 kW, 16 A

29. 12 W, 4.7 V

30. 120 W, 170 V

31. (a) 1.7 A, 5.0 A
    (b) 140 Ω, 48 Ω

32. (a) 50 W, 14 W
    (b) 2.9 Ω, 10 Ω

33. (a) $2(440) = 880$ mA
    (b) $(0.75)(440) = 330$ mA
    (c) $\left(\dfrac{1}{2}\right)(440) = 220$ mA

34. (a) $\left(\dfrac{1}{3}\right)(60) = 40$ W
    (b) $(0.50)(60) = 30$ W

35. (a) 15 kW
    (b) 810 Ω

36. (a) 200 V
    (b) 2.0 kΩ

37. (a) 170 mW
    (b) 1.1 V

38. (a) 570 mΩ
    (b) 88 A

39. 3.1 W, 2.4 W, 5.5 W

40. 1.1 W, 0.74 W, 1.8 W

41. (a) 81 V
    (b) $(0.050)(24) = 1.2$ kWh $= 4.3$ MJ

42. (a) 1.9 A
    (b) $(1.5)(12) = 18$ kWh $= 65$ MJ

43. 360 W, 160 W, 520 W

44. 18 mW, 8.9 mW, 27 mW

45. $P = VI = V\left(\dfrac{V}{R}\right) = \dfrac{V^2}{R}$

46. $P = \dfrac{V^2}{R} \rightarrow PR = V^2 \rightarrow R = \dfrac{V^2}{P}$;
    $P = \dfrac{V^2}{R} \rightarrow PR = V^2 \rightarrow V = \sqrt{PR}$

Review Exercises

1. 300 mA, 11 W

2. 2.7 A, 3.8 kW

3. 90 Ω, 900 mW

4. 42 Ω, 290 W

5. 180 V, 400 W

6. 44 V, 1.5 W

7. 1.3 A, 64 Ω

8. 820 mA, 6.7 Ω

9. 33 V, 74 kΩ

10. 470 V, 31 Ω

11. 2.2 kV, 3.0 A

12. 300 V, 40 mA

13. (a) 500 mA
    (b) $(1.5)(500) = 750$ mA
    (c) 50%, I is directly proportional to V_S

14. (a) 600 mA
    (b) $\left(\dfrac{1}{2}\right)(600) = 300$ mA
    (c) I changes by $\dfrac{1}{2}$;
        I is inversely proportional to R

15. (a) 9.0 V
    (b) $\left(\dfrac{1}{2}\right)(9.0) = 4.5$ V

16. (a) $(150\%)(200) = 300$ mA
    (b) $\left(\dfrac{1}{2}\right)(200) = 100$ mA

17. $\dfrac{(12 - 10)}{(30 - 20)} = \dfrac{\Delta R}{(60 - 20)} \rightarrow \Delta R$
    $= 8 \rightarrow R = 18$ Ω

18. $\left(\dfrac{1.0}{0.50}\right)(10) = 20$ μF

19. (a) 200 mA
    (b) $(0.05)(72) = 3.6$ kWh $= 13$ MJ

20. (a) 180 V, 320 kΩ
    (b) $(2)(100) = 200$ mW

21. (a) 670 mΩ
    (b) 60 A

22. (a) 57 W, 16 W
    (b) 73 W

23. $\dfrac{1500}{500} = \dfrac{3}{1}$

24. (a) $(2)(100) = 200$ W
    (b) $(1.5)(100) = 150$ W

CHAPTER 9 Multiplying and Factoring Polynomials

Exercise 9.1 Multiplying Polynomials

1. $x^2 + 6x + 8$

2. $R^2 - 4R - 5$

3. $C^2 + 3C - 4$

4. $a^2 - 7a + 12$

5. $l^2 - 100$

6. $m^2 - 25$

7. $2V^2 - V - 10$

8. $2y^2 - 8y - 24$

9. $t^2 - 8t + 16$

10. $G^2 - 6G + 9$

11. $4P^2 - 2P - 20$

12. $10f^2 - 7fg + g^2$

13. $V_1^2 - 9$

14. $4R_2^2 - 1$

15. $6X^2 - 7XR + 2R^2$

16. $4a^2 - 13ab - 35b^2$

17. $4x^2 + 12x + 9$

18. $9k^2 - 12k + 4$

19. $25L^2 - 4C^2$

20. $d^2 - 4e^2$

21. $16y^2 - 9$

22. $25s^2 - 36t^2$

23. $3a^2 - 3b^2$

24. $5l^2 - 5R^2$

25. $2C^2 + 4CL + 2L^2$

26. $3X^2 - 12X + 12$

27. $E^3 - E^2 - E + 1$

28. $c^3 + c^2d - cd^2 - d^3$

29. $L^3 - 3L^2 + 5L - 6$

30. $2Q^3 + 3Q^2 - 3Q - 4$

31. $T^3 - 1$

32. $x^3 + y^3$

33. $(n + 3)(n - 2) = n^2 + n - 6$

34. $(2w - 3)(2w + 3) = 4w^2 - 9$

35. $(l - 5)^2 = l^2 - 10l + 25$

36. $\pi(a + 1)^2 = \pi a^2 + 2\pi a + \pi$

37. $(t + 4)(2t + 2) = 2t^2 + 10t + 8$

38. $(2t - 3)(3t + 1) = 6t^2 - 7t - 3$

39. $0.03T^2 + 0.28T - 24$

40. $(t + 4)^2(10) = (T^2 + 8t + 16)(10)$
$= 10t^2 + 80t + 160$

Exercise 9.2 Monomial Factors

1. $(2)(2)(3)(3)$

2. $(2)(3)(5)(5)$

3. $(2)(2)(7)(x)(y)(y)$

4. $(-2)(2)(17)(a)(a)(b)(b)$

5. $(-3)(13)(R_1)(R_2)$

6. $(3)(19)(V)(V)(I)(I)$

7. $5(R + 3)$

8. $3(4V - 1)$

9. $a(a - 2)$

10. $x(2x + 1)$

11. $p^2(3p + 1)$

12. $f^2(f - 10)$

13. $0.5V(I_1 - 0.5I_2)$

14. $0.2r(s^2 + 2t^2)$

15. $3.3XY(2Y + 1)$

16. $0.5wL(3 - 5L)$

17. $2I^2(2R_1 + R_2)$

18. $pq(q - p)$

19. $\left(\dfrac{4}{b}\right)(3a + 4)$

20. $\left(\dfrac{x}{25}\right)(1 - x)$

21. $\left(\dfrac{4}{I}\right)(P_1 + 2P_2)$

22. $5V\left(\dfrac{2}{R_1} - \dfrac{1}{R_2}\right)$

23. $5(2s^2 + 4s - 3)$

24. $6(2m^2 - 3m + 2)$

25. $4v(6v^2 - 4v + 3)$

26. $10h^2(2h^2 + 5h - 1)$

27. $6ab(4a^2 - 5ab + 7b^2)$

28. $9cd(4d^2 + 2cd + 3c^2)$

29. $xyz(x + y + z)$

30. $RST(RS - RT - ST)$

31. $14R(4I_1^2 + 3I_2^2)$

32. $25V^2\left(\dfrac{2}{R_1} + \dfrac{1}{R_2}\right)$

33. $\left(\dfrac{e^{-1}}{R}\right)(V - V_0)$

34. $\left(\dfrac{V}{R}\right)(1 - e^{-1})$

Exercise 9.3 Binomial Factors

1. $(a + 2b)(a - 2b)$

2. $(4x + 5y)(4x - 5y)$

3. $(X + 0.4)(X - 0.4)$

4. $(0.2 + f)(0.2 - f)$

5. $(0.5X + Y)(0.5X - Y)$

6. $(1 + 0.6A)(1 - 0.6A)$

7. $(Z + 1)(Z + 5)$

8. $(d + 1)(d + 2)$

9. $(v - 1)(v - 3)$

10. $(E - 2)(E - 6)$

11. $(C_1 + 3)^2$

12. $(V_T + 8)^2$

13. prime

14. prime

15. $(A - 4)^2$

16. $(2B - 1)^2$

17. $(n + 1)(n - 7)$

18. $(p + 2)(p - 6)$

19. $50(m + 2)(m - 2)$

20. $3(h + 3)(h - 3)$

21. $(3G + 1)(G + 1)$

22. $(2f + 1)(f + 3)$

23. $(4e - 1)(e - 1)$

24. $(3Q - 1)(Q - 3)$

25. $(2x + 1)(x - 3)$

26. $(2y + 1)(y - 7)$

27. $(5x + 6y)(x - y)$

28. $(4a + b)(2a - 3b)$

29. prime

30. prime

31. $4(2R - 1)(R + 4)$

32. $2(3t + 5)(t - 1)$

33. $2(x + 2y)(x - 2y)$

34. $5(R + 4)(R - 4)$

35. $5P(2V + 5)(V - 1)$

36. $2u(v + 1)(v + 5)$

37. $(S - 0.3)^2$

38. $(V_0 + 0.5)^2$

39. $(L^2 + 1)^2$

40. $(I^2 - 2)^2$

41. $\left(\dfrac{1}{2}\right)(T^2 - 25) = \left(\dfrac{1}{2}\right)(T + 5)(T - 5)$

42. $2\left(\dfrac{m^2}{n^2} - 4\right) = 2\left(\dfrac{m}{n} + 2\right)\left(\dfrac{m}{n} - 2\right)$

43. $4(t + 3)(t + 4)$

44. $t(2t + 1)(t - 2)$

45. $(0.5t - 1.0)^2$

46. $4(t + 1)(t - 1)$

47. $R(I_1 + I_2)(I_1 - I_2)$

48. $\left(\dfrac{1}{R}\right)(V_1 + V_2)(V_1 - V_2)$

49. $X^2Y - X_0^2Y = Y(X + X_0)(X - X_0)$

50. $K^2T^2 - 2KTT_1 + T_1^2 = (KT - T_1)^2$

Exercise 9.4   Second-Degree Equations

1. ± 2

2. ± 4

3. $\pm\dfrac{3}{7}$

4. $\pm\dfrac{5}{2} = \pm 2.50$

5. $5, -2$

6. $-2, -4$

7. $1, -\dfrac{1}{3} = -0.333$

8. $1, \dfrac{3}{2} = 1.50$

9. $\dfrac{1}{2}, \dfrac{1}{2} = 0.50$

10. $-3, -3$

11. $2, \dfrac{2}{3} = 0.667$

12. $1, -\dfrac{7}{5} = -1.40$

13. $0, \dfrac{1}{7} = 0.143$

14. $0, -\dfrac{9}{5} = -1.80$

15. $\pm\dfrac{8}{5} = \pm 1.60$

16. $\pm\dfrac{11}{15} = \pm 0.733$

17. ± 0.740

18. ± 0.853

19. $-1, \dfrac{1}{2} = 0.50$

20. $2, \frac{4}{3} = 1.33$

21. $2, -\frac{5}{3} = -1.67$

22. $3, \frac{1}{2} = 0.50$

23. $0.193, -5.19$

24. $0.414, -2.41$

25. $1.62, -0.618$

26. $2.30, -1.30$

27. $2.41, -0.414$

28. $0.303, -3.30$

29. $1.28, -0.781$

30. $1.37, -0.366$

31. $3.65, -1.65$

32. $0.281, -1.78$

33. $1.31, 0.191$

34. $3.68, -0.679$

35. $1.58, 0.423$

36. $9.32, -0.322$

37. $s^2 + (2s)^2 = 8^2 \rightarrow s = \sqrt{\dfrac{64}{5}} = 3.6$ ft,
$\rightarrow$ hypotenuse $= 7.2$ ft

38. $s^2 + 5^2 = (3s)^2 \rightarrow s = \sqrt{\dfrac{25}{8}} = 1.8$ m,
$\rightarrow$ hypotenuse $= 5.3$ m

39. $w(w + 10) = 96 \rightarrow w = 6$ ft, $l = 16$ ft

40. $w(w + 1) = 0.56 \rightarrow w = 0.40$ m $= 40$ cm,
$l = 1.4$ m $= 140$ cm

41. $3500\ \Omega = 3.5\ k\Omega$

42. $6600\ \Omega = 6.6\ k\Omega$

43. 5.0 A, 8.0 A

44. 0.59 A, 3.4 A

45. 0.89 A, 0.11 A

46. 1.3 A, 0.39 A

Review Exercises

1. $W^2 - 2W - 8$

2. $6E_1^2 + 17E_1 - 10$

3. $0.02k^2 + 0.03k - 0.02$

4. $49f^2 + 140f + 100$

5. $4m^2 - 1$

6. $25N^2 - 16$

7. $3X^2 - 3Y^2$

8. $5a^2 - 10ab + 5b^2$

9. $I^3 - 2I^2 - 4I + 8$

10. $R^3 + R^2 - R - 1$

11. $2x(x - 2)$

12. $r^2(r + 3)$

13. $12C(A^2 + B^2)$

14. $40I^2(3R + 4R_0)$

15. $3z(7z^2 + 5z - 9)$

16. $15v^2(v^2 + 3v - 2)$

17. $\left(\dfrac{3}{R}\right)(V_1 + 3V_2)$

18. $rst(r + s + t)$

19. $(4x + 5y)(4x - 5y)$

20. $(f + 0.1)(f - 0.1)$

21. $\left(10 + \dfrac{A}{2}\right)\left(10 - \dfrac{A}{2}\right)$

22. $(l - 1)(l - 5)$

23. $(P + 7)(P - 3)$

24. $4(2C - 1)^2$

25. $(X + 0.1)(X + 0.2)$

26. $10(n - 2)(n + 2)$

27. $(2q - 3)(q - 1)$

28. $(3R - 5)(R + 3)$

29. $(2u - 3v)(3u - 2v)$

30. $6(2t + 1)(t + 2)$

31. $5(5X - 2)(X + 1)$

32. $\left(\dfrac{1}{10}\right)(s + 3)(s - 3)$

33. ± 4

34. $\pm\dfrac{2}{5} = \pm 0.40$

35. $5, -1$

36. $\frac{2}{3} = 0.667, -1$

37. $0, \frac{7}{8} = 0.875$

38. $0, 25$

39. ± 2.10

40. $2, \frac{4}{3} = 1.33$

41. $5, -10$

42. $\frac{3}{4} = 0.75, \frac{3}{4} = 0.75$

43. $2, 2$

44. $\frac{1}{3} = 0.333, -1$

45. $3.73, 0.268$

46. $0.414, -2.41$

47. $2.62, 0.382$

48. $0.839, -0.239$

49. $0.809, -0.309$

50. $0.873, -0.573$

51. $1.70, -2.68$

52. $2.47, -0.808$

53. $(3l - 2)(2l + 3) = 6l^2 + 5l - 6$

54. $\dfrac{\theta r_1^2}{2} - \dfrac{\theta r_2^2}{2}$

55. $6(t + 3)(t + 4)$

56. $\left(\dfrac{m}{2}\right)(v_2 + v_1)(v_2 - v_1)$

57. $w(w + 5) = 600 \rightarrow w = 22$ cm, $l = 27$ cm

58. $s^2 + (1.5s)^2 = 4^2 \rightarrow s = 2.2$ cm, $1.5s = 3.3$ cm

59. $(2t - 3)(t + 5) = 2t^2 + 7t - 15$

60. $(t - 5)^2(3.0) = 3t^2 - 30t + 75$

61. $25R(3I_1 + 5I_2)$

62. $\left(\dfrac{1}{2}\right)\left(\dfrac{V_2}{2} + V_1\right)\left(\dfrac{V_2}{2} - V_1\right)$

63. 5.0 A

64. 7.3 A, 0.65 A

65. 3.1 kΩ

66. $I_L = 2.5$ A, $I_R = 3.7$ A

67. 2 A, 4 A

68. 3 A

CHAPTER 10   Algebraic Fractions

Exercise 10.1   Reducing Fractions

1. $\dfrac{5}{2x}$

2. $\dfrac{2y}{5}$

3. $\dfrac{7a^2}{9}$

4. $\dfrac{2}{5b}$

5. $\dfrac{a + b}{a}$

6. $\dfrac{T - 1}{T}$

7. $\dfrac{L}{M - N}$

8. $\dfrac{B + D}{C}$

9. $\dfrac{q}{p + 1}$

10. $\dfrac{x + y}{x}$

11. $\dfrac{R_1 - R_2}{5}$

12. $\dfrac{1}{2(x - y)}$

13. 3

14. $\frac{5}{3}$

15. $\dfrac{2V + 1}{2}$

16. $\dfrac{1}{P - 1}$

17. $\dfrac{t + 3}{3t - 1}$

18. $\dfrac{d - 2}{3d + 1}$

19. not reducible

20. not reducible

21. $\dfrac{2a + x}{2a - x}$

22. $\dfrac{b - 2y}{b - y}$

23. $\dfrac{7X_L - 1}{9X_L - 4}$

24. $\dfrac{6P + 1}{11P + 4}$

25. $\dfrac{2(2f - 3)}{f - 3}$

26. $\dfrac{8(e - 1)}{e - 2}$

27. $\dfrac{3(F_x - F_y)(F_x + F_y)}{1.5(F_x - F_y)} = 2(F_x + F_y)$

28. $\dfrac{8l(3l + w)(l - w)}{2(3l + w)} = 4l(l - w)$

29. $\dfrac{4(2t + 1)(2t - 1)}{4(2t - 1)} = 2t + 1$

30. $\dfrac{(I - 2)(I + 2)}{2(I - 2)} = \dfrac{I + 2}{2}$

Exercise 10.2 Multiplying and Dividing Fractions

1. $\dfrac{6}{x}$

2. $\dfrac{y}{4}$

3. $\dfrac{1}{y}$

4. $\dfrac{3}{rt^2}$

5. $\dfrac{1}{2}$

6. $\dfrac{Z}{2}$

7. $\dfrac{5b}{a}$

8. $\dfrac{1}{5t}$

9. $\dfrac{5g(g-h)}{14h}$

10. $\dfrac{7}{uv}$

11. $\dfrac{s-t}{s}$

12. $(w+10)(w+10)$

13. 4

14. 1

15. $\dfrac{I_2}{5(I_1-I_2)}$

16. $\dfrac{V_2}{V_1(V_2+V_1)}$

17. $2(a+1)$

18. $2c-3$

19. $5(2D-1)$

20. $\dfrac{2m-3n}{2n}$

21. $\dfrac{R_2}{R_1^2}$

22. $\dfrac{V_0+1}{V_0}$

23. $\dfrac{2x(y+2)}{3}$

24. $\dfrac{5}{b}$

25. $\dfrac{10^3}{K}$

26. $\dfrac{2\times10^3 N}{3}$

27. 1

28. $\dfrac{c}{d}$

29. $\dfrac{4r}{3\pi}$

30. $3h$

31. $P=VI=V\left(\dfrac{V}{R}\right)=\dfrac{V^2}{R}$

32. $R=\dfrac{V}{I}=\dfrac{P}{I}\div(I)=\left(\dfrac{P}{I}\right)\left(\dfrac{1}{I}\right)=\dfrac{P}{I^2}$

33. $\dfrac{R_1(3R_1)}{R_1+3R_1}=\dfrac{3R_1}{4}$

34. $\dfrac{2R_2(R_2)}{2R_2+R_2}=\dfrac{2R_2}{3}$

Exercise 10.3 Addition of Fractions

1. $\dfrac{4x}{5}$

2. $\dfrac{y}{5}$

3. $\dfrac{1}{3a}$

4. $\dfrac{4}{t}$

5. $\dfrac{5R+9}{60}$

6. $\dfrac{4+15V}{90}$

7. $\dfrac{35-12I}{40}$

8. $\dfrac{10K+12}{45}$

9. $\dfrac{17}{63z}$

10. $\dfrac{52}{75m}$

11. $\dfrac{37p}{45}$

12. $\dfrac{2q}{35}$

13. $\dfrac{5t}{2s}$

14. $\dfrac{17a}{5I_1}$

15. $\dfrac{6-8w}{rw^2}$

16. $\dfrac{5k+6x}{kx^2}$

17. $\dfrac{4V_1^2+3V_2^2}{V_1V_2}$

18. $\dfrac{6R_1^2-2R^2}{RR_1}$

19. $\dfrac{2X-3XY}{12Y^2}$

20. $\dfrac{5AK+6A}{16K^2}$

21. $\dfrac{27+25d}{30cd^2}$

22. $\dfrac{4k+35m}{5m^2k^2}$

23. $\dfrac{100}{4\times10^4}-\dfrac{75}{4\times10^4}=\dfrac{25}{4\times10^4}$ or $\dfrac{1}{16\times10^2}$

24. $\dfrac{30}{9\times10^6}+\dfrac{5}{9\times10^6}=\dfrac{35}{9\times10^6}$ or $\dfrac{7}{18\times10^5}$

25. $\dfrac{5x+2}{x(x+1)}$

26. $\dfrac{y+3}{y(y-1)}$

27. $\dfrac{4+3h-h^2}{h(h+2)}$

28. $\dfrac{f^2+6f-9}{f(f-3)}$

29. $\dfrac{2d^2+6cd-5c^2}{2d^2}$

30. $\dfrac{3w^2-2wx+x^2}{wx}$

31. $\dfrac{5xy - 2}{10y^2}$

32. $\dfrac{18ab + 5}{6b^2}$

33. $\dfrac{8.1 + 2.3V}{I(1 + V)}$

34. $\dfrac{0.46N - 0.15}{P(1 - n)}$

35. $\dfrac{4V + 1}{2(V + 1)}$

36. $\dfrac{6R + 4}{(R + 1)(R - 1)}$

37. $\dfrac{4 - t}{(t + 1)(t - 1)}$

38. $\dfrac{1}{v + 2}$

39. $\dfrac{4D - 3(D + 1) + (D + 3)}{3D} = \dfrac{2D}{3D} = \dfrac{2}{3}$

40. $\dfrac{2(X - 1) + (X + 2) - X}{2X} = \dfrac{2X}{2X} = 1$

41. $\dfrac{(3r - 5) - 4(r - 1)}{(r + 1)(r - 1)} = \dfrac{-1(r + 1)}{(r + 1)(r - 1)} = \dfrac{-1}{r - 1} = \dfrac{1}{1 - r}$

42. $\dfrac{2n^2 - k(k - n)}{(k + n)(k - n)} = \dfrac{(2n - k)(k + n)}{(k + n)(k - n)} = \dfrac{2n - k}{k - n}$

43. $\dfrac{7I_1^2 + 9I_1I_2 - I_2^2}{I_1I_2(I_1 + I_2)}$

44. $\dfrac{5V_2^2 + 2V_1V_2 - 8V_1^2}{V_1V_2(V_2 - V_1)}$

45. $\dfrac{a^2 + b^2}{b^2} = \dfrac{c^2}{b^2}$

46. $\dfrac{5k + 3}{k(k + 2)}$

47. $\dfrac{R_1R_2}{R_1 + R_2}$

48. $\dfrac{I_TR_2 + I_TR_1}{R_1 + R_2} = \dfrac{I_T(R_1 + R_2)}{R_1 + R_2} = I_T$

49. $\dfrac{6}{R_1} + \dfrac{3}{R_2} = \dfrac{6R_2 + 3R_1}{R_1R_2}$

50. $\dfrac{6}{R_1} + \dfrac{6}{R_1 + R_2} = \dfrac{12R_1 + 6R_2}{R_1(R_1 + R_2)}$

51. $\dfrac{R_1R_2R_3}{R_1R_2 + R_1R_3 + R_2R_3}$

52. $\dfrac{V(2R_1 + 100)}{R_1(R_1 + 100)}$

Exercise 10.4   Equations with Fractions

1. 12

2. 1.5

3. 20

4. 1.5

5. 2

6. 4

7. 1

8. 2

9. 5

10. 3

11. 0.5

12. 1.5

13. 100

14. $\frac{10}{3} = 3.3$

15. 2.5

16. 50

17. $\frac{1}{5} = 0.2$

18. 0.25

19. −4

20. $-\frac{1}{3} = -0.33$

21. 6

22. 120

23. 12

24. 48

25. 0.4

26. 3

27. 30

28. 10

29. 4.5

30. 4

31. 4

32. 1.5

33. 3.2

34. 600

35. $10G - 2G - 6 = 3G + 9 \rightarrow G = 3$

36. $5Z - 20 + 3Z = 20Z - 80 \rightarrow Z = 5$

37. $2w^2 - w + w + 3 = 2w^2 + 6w \rightarrow w = \frac{1}{2} = 0.5$

38. $3f^2 - 3f^2 + 6f = 5f - 10 \rightarrow f = -10$

39. 7

40. 8

41. $100

42. $\dfrac{2400}{F_1} = \dfrac{6400}{100} \rightarrow F_1 = 38 \text{ kg}$

43. 260 Ω

44. 900 Ω

45. 1.3 kΩ = 1300 Ω

46. 20 Ω

47. $\dfrac{20}{R_4 - R_3} = \dfrac{80}{100} \rightarrow R_4 - R_3 = 25 \text{ m}\Omega$

48. 60 mA

Review Exercises

1. $5x^2$

2. $4W - 3$

3. $\dfrac{5}{a + 4b}$

4. $\dfrac{5R_1 - R_2}{5}$

5. $\dfrac{2f - 1}{2f + 1}$

6. $\dfrac{3y - 1}{3y + 1}$

7. $\dfrac{16x}{45}$

8. $\dfrac{9V}{10}$

9. 1

10. $\dfrac{5c(0.5c - d)}{d}$

11. 3

12. $\dfrac{1}{n - d}$

13. $\dfrac{R_1 + 2R_2}{2R_1 + R_2}$

14. $\dfrac{6P}{V}$

15. 5

16. $\dfrac{y(y - 2)}{2y - 1}$

17. $\dfrac{21}{5x}$

18. $\dfrac{-D}{60}$

19. $\dfrac{23}{15r}$

20. $\dfrac{t(14V_2 + 11V_1)}{2V_1 V_2}$

21. $\dfrac{15b - 6a}{14a^2 b^2}$

22. $\dfrac{10}{6 \times 10^4} + \dfrac{1}{6 \times 10^4} = \dfrac{11}{6 \times 10^4}$

23. $\dfrac{9x - 1}{2x(x - 1)}$

24. $\dfrac{10k^2 - 15mk - 9m^2}{15mk}$

25. $\dfrac{0.66 - 0.44r}{t(1 - r)}$

26. $\dfrac{1 - 2a + 2x}{(a + x)(a - x)}$

27. $\dfrac{(5m - 5) - 10m - 10 - 6m}{10m} = \dfrac{-11m - 15}{10m}$

28. $$\frac{5R_1 R_2 - 3R_1(R_1 - R_2) + R_2(R_1 - R_2)}{R_1 R_2(R_1 - R_2)}$$

$$= \frac{-3R_1^2 + 9R_1 R_2 - R_2^2}{R_1 R_2(R_1 - R_2)}$$

29. 8

30. $0.05 = \frac{1}{20}$

31. 150

32. 23

33. 7

34. −12

35. 6.7

36. 60

37. −2

38. 72

39. $5P = 2P + 2 + 2P \rightarrow P = 2$

40. $9V_1 + 9 - 12V_1 = V_1 + 1 \rightarrow V_1 = 2$

41. $4.5h$

42. (a) $\dfrac{2D(r_1 r_2)}{Dr_1 + Dr_2} = \dfrac{2r_1 r_2}{r_1 + r_2}$

(b) 24 mi/h

43. $\dfrac{2t}{t - 1}[(0.5t(t - 1)] = t^2$

44. $\left[\dfrac{4t^2}{(t - 1)^2}\right]\left[\dfrac{(t + 1)(t - 1)}{t^2}\right] = \dfrac{4(t + 1)}{t - 1}$

45. $\dfrac{R_2(2R_2 + 3R_3)}{R_2 + R_3}$

46. $\dfrac{V(90 + R_1)}{15(R_1 + 75)}$

47. 60 μF

48. 150 pF

49. 2.0 mH

50. 2.0 H

51. $150 = 90 + \dfrac{150R_2}{R_2 + 150} \rightarrow 150R_2 + 22{,}500$

$= 90R_2 + 13{,}500 + 150R_2 \rightarrow R_2 = 100 \ \Omega$

52. $18 = 12 + \dfrac{2R_2^2}{3R_2} \rightarrow 54 = 36 + 2R_2 \rightarrow$

$R_2 = 9 \ \Omega, \ R_3 = 18 \ \Omega$

CHAPTER 11   Formulas and Problem Solving

Exercise 11.1   Formulas and Literal Equations

1. $I = \dfrac{P}{V}$

2. $P = VI$

3. $P = I^2 R$

4. $P = \dfrac{V^2}{R}$

5. $m = \dfrac{F}{a}$

6. $t = \dfrac{v - v_0}{a}$

7. $f = \dfrac{1}{2\pi X_C C}$

8. $e = \dfrac{Cd}{A}$

9. $V = \sqrt{PR}$

10. $I = \sqrt{\dfrac{P}{R}}$

11. $r = \sqrt{\dfrac{A}{\pi}}$

12. $s = \sqrt{2A}$

13. $r_g = \dfrac{V - IR}{I}$

14. $V_1 = \dfrac{P - IV_2}{I}$

15. $w = \dfrac{P - 2l}{2}$

16. $l = \dfrac{A - 2w^2}{4w}$

17. $I = \dfrac{V - V_0}{R}$

18. $V_0 = AB - AV$

19. $P = V(I_1 + I_2) \rightarrow V = \dfrac{P}{I_1 + I_2}$

20. $I(R_1 + R_2) = I_0 R_0 \rightarrow I = \dfrac{I_0 R_0}{R_1 + R_2}$

21. $V_T = I(R_1 + R_2 + R_3) \rightarrow I = \dfrac{V_T}{R_1 + R_2 + R_3}$

22. $P_T = V(I_1 + I_2 + I_3) \rightarrow V = \dfrac{P_T}{I_1 + I_2 + I_3}$

23. $I_C \beta + I_C = \beta I_E \rightarrow \beta(I_E - I_C)$

$= I_C \rightarrow \beta = \dfrac{I_C}{I_E - I_C}$

24. $I_1 G_1 + I_1 G_2 = I_T G_1 \rightarrow G_1(I_T - I_1)$

$= I_1 G_2 \rightarrow G_1 = \dfrac{I_1 G_2}{I_T - I_1}$

25. $R_2 = \dfrac{R_{eq} R_1}{R_1 - R_{eq}}$

26. $L_1 = \dfrac{L_T L_2}{L_2 - L_T}$

27. $L_1 L_2 = L_T L_2 + L_T L_1 \rightarrow L_2(L_1 - L_T)$

$= L_T L_1 \rightarrow L_2 = \dfrac{L_T L_1}{L_1 - L_T}$

28. $R_1 = \dfrac{R_{eq} R_2}{R_2 - R_{eq}}$

29. $\dfrac{Z}{wL} - ZwC = 1 \rightarrow Z - Zw^2 CL = wL \rightarrow$

$Z = L(w + w^2 CZ) \rightarrow L = \dfrac{Z}{w(1 + wCZ)}$

30. $R_A = \dfrac{R_{AB}(R_B + R_C)}{R_B - R_{AB}}$

31. (a) $h = 116{,}600 - 550T$

(b) 1100 ft

32. (a) $t = \dfrac{v - v_0}{g}$

(b) $t = \dfrac{22.5 - 7.5}{9.8} \rightarrow t = 1.5$ s

33. (a) $C = \left(\dfrac{5}{9}\right)(F - 32)$

(b) $F = 45,\ C = 7.2;\ F = 90,$
$C = 32.2 \rightarrow \Delta F = 25°C$

34. (a) $\Delta F = \left[\left(\dfrac{9}{5}\right)C_2 + 32\right] - \left[\left(\dfrac{9}{5}\right)C_1 + 32\right] \rightarrow$

$\Delta F = \left(\dfrac{9}{5}\right)\Delta C = 1.8\Delta C$

(b) $\Delta F = 1.8(50) = 90°F$

35. $P = (IR)I = I^2 R$

36. $R = \dfrac{P/I}{I} = \dfrac{P}{I^2}$

37. $P = V\left(\dfrac{V}{R}\right) = \dfrac{V^2}{R} \rightarrow \left(\dfrac{R}{P}\right)P$

$= \left(\dfrac{R}{P}\right)\left(\dfrac{V^2}{R}\right) \rightarrow R = \dfrac{V^2}{P}$

38. $P = \left(\dfrac{V}{R}\right)^2 (R) = \dfrac{V^2}{R}$

39. (a) $R_1 = \dfrac{V - V_0}{I}$

(b) 6.0 Ω

40. (a) $I = \dfrac{V - V_0}{R_1}$

(b) 0.02A = 20 mA

41. $R_x = \dfrac{R_1 R_{eq}}{R_1 - R_{eq}}$

42. $R_x = \dfrac{R_1 R_{eq}}{R_1 - R_{eq}}$

43. (a) $\alpha = \dfrac{R_t - R_0}{R_0 t}$

(b) $\dfrac{0.0031}{°C}$

44. (a) $R_t = R_0(1 + \alpha t) \rightarrow R_0 = \dfrac{R_t}{1 + \alpha t}$

(b) 330 Ω

45. (a) $\rho = \dfrac{RA}{l}$

(b) 2.1×10^{-8} Ω–m

46. (a) $R_T = \dfrac{2R_1 R_2}{R_1 + 2R_2}$

(b) 10 kΩ

47. $4\pi^2 f^2 LC = 1 \rightarrow f^2 = \dfrac{1}{4\pi^2 f^2 LC} \rightarrow$

$f = \dfrac{1}{2\pi\sqrt{LC}}$

48. (a) $P_T = I^2(R_1 + R_2) \rightarrow I = \sqrt{\dfrac{P_T}{R_1 + R_2}}$

  (b) $\dfrac{1}{6}$ A $= 0.17$ A

49. (a) $(1.1)(80) - (1.3)(80) = -16V$

  (b) $\Delta V = I_2 R - I_1 R = R(\Delta I)$
  (c) $\Delta V = 80(-0.2) = -16$ V
  (d) $\Delta V = 80(0.4) = 32$ V

50. (a) $\Delta P = V_2(I_2 - I_1) = V_S(\Delta I)$
  (b) $\Delta P = 110(1.5 - 1.7) = -22$ W

51. (a) $\Delta V = 2IR - IR = IR$
  (b) $\Delta V = 0.9IR - IR = -0.1IR$

52. (a) $\Delta P = 1.5 V_S I - V_S I = 0.5 V_S I$
  (b) $\Delta P = V_S I - 0.5 V_S I = -0.5 V_S I$

Exercise 11.2   Problem Solving

1. \$42,500, \$53,500

2. \$150, \$450

3. $1.1S = 58,500 \rightarrow S = \$53,182$

4. $1.08P = 32.39 \rightarrow P = \$29.99$

5. $P - \left(\dfrac{1}{3P}\right) = 28 \rightarrow P = \$42$

6. $0.4V = 4300 \rightarrow V = \$10,750$

7. $\dfrac{73 + 78 + T}{3} = 80 \rightarrow T = 89$

8. $\left(\dfrac{2}{3}\right)77 + \left(\dfrac{1}{3}\right)F = 80 \rightarrow F = 86$

9. **(a)** $1.15C = 3000 \rightarrow C = \$2608.70$
   (b) $3000 - 1.05(2608.70) = \$260.87$

10. **(a)** $1.085P = 864 \rightarrow P = \$796.31$
    (b) $864 - 1.05(796.31) = \$27.87$

11. 1925 lines/min

12. 2.4 min, 1.6 min

13. $4(4) = 2r \rightarrow r = 8$ mi/h

14. $5(1.5) = 2.5r \rightarrow r = 3$ mi/h

15. $30(t + 1) = 50t \rightarrow t = 1.5$ h

16. $3(t + 2) = 12t \rightarrow t = \left(\dfrac{2}{3}\right)$h $= 40$ min

17. $L_1 + 1.1L_1 = 11 \rightarrow L_1 = 5.2$ mH, $L_2 = 5.8$ mH

18. $0.8L_2 + L_2 = 360 \rightarrow L_2 = 200$ µH, $L_1 = 160$ µH

19. $I_1 + 1.5I_1 + 3I_1 = 275 \rightarrow I_1 = 50$ mA, $I_2 = 75$ mA, $I_3 = 150$ mA

20. $36 + \dfrac{I_T}{3} + \dfrac{I_T}{6} = I_T \rightarrow I_T = 72$ mA, $I_2 = 24$ mA, $I_3 = 12$ mA

21. 6.0 V, 5.7 V

22. 6250 MW, 6250 MW, 7500 MW

23. $l + 0.75l = 350 \rightarrow l = 200$ cm, $0.75l = 150$ cm

24. $l + 2l + 2(2l) = 7(12) \rightarrow l = 12$ in, $2l = 24$ in, $4l = 48$ in

25. $V_1 + 2V_1\left(\dfrac{V_1}{3}\right) = 70 \rightarrow V_1 = 21$ V, $V_2 = 42$ V, $V_3 = 7.0$ V

26. $\dfrac{V_2}{2} + V_2 + 1.5V_2 = 70 \rightarrow V_1 = 12$ V, $V_2 = 23$ V, $V_3 = 35$ V

27. $4I_3 + 2I_3 = I_3 + 5 \rightarrow I_1 = 4$ A, $I_2 = 2$ A, $I_3 = 1$ A

28. $I_1 = 7$ A, $I_2 = 3.5$ A, $I_4 = 5.5$ A

29. $V_R + 1.5V_R = 12 \rightarrow V_R = 4.8$ V, $V_B = 7.2$ V

30. 6.0 W

31. $1.25N = 45 \rightarrow N = 36$

32. $\dfrac{1.25}{1.7} = \dfrac{45}{N} \rightarrow N = 61$

Review Exercises

1. $Q = \dfrac{Er^2}{k}$

2. $I_S = \dfrac{I_M R_M}{R_S}$

3. $r = \sqrt{\dfrac{Q_1 Q_2}{F}}$

4. $I = \dfrac{P}{(V_1 + V_2)}$

5. $a = \dfrac{2(d - v_0 t)}{t^2}$

6. $C_1 = \dfrac{C_T C_2}{C_2 - C_T}$

7. $L_1 = \dfrac{L_T L_2}{L_2 - L_T}$

8. $V_{TH}(R_S + R_L) = R_L V_S \rightarrow$

   $V_{TH} R_S = R_L(V_S - V_{TH}) \rightarrow R_L = \dfrac{V_{TH} R_S}{V_S - V_{TH}}$

9. (a) $t = \dfrac{l_t - l_0}{10.7 \times 10^{-6} l_0}$

   (b) $t = \dfrac{0.01 l_0}{10.7 \times 10^{-6} l_0} \rightarrow t = 934.6°\,C$

10. $0.65p = 325 \rightarrow p = \$500$

11. $1.05p = 30 \rightarrow p = \$28.57$

12. $40t + 50t = 180 \rightarrow t = 2.0$ h

13. $\left(\dfrac{m_0}{2m_0}\right)^2 = 1 - \dfrac{v^2}{(3 \times 10^8)^2} \rightarrow$

   $\dfrac{v^2}{(3 \times 10^8)^2} = \dfrac{3}{4} \rightarrow v = 2.6 \times 10^8$ m/s

14. (a) 4.4°C
    (b) −40°

15. (a) $I = \dfrac{V_2 - V_1}{R_1 + R_2}$

    (b) 0.80 A = 800 mA

16. $P = V\left(\dfrac{V}{R}\right) = \dfrac{V^2}{R} \rightarrow V^2$

    $= PR \rightarrow V = \sqrt{PR}$

17. (a) $R_T = \dfrac{R_1 + R_2^2}{2R_2} \rightarrow R_T - R_1 = \dfrac{R_2}{2} \rightarrow$

    $R_2 = 2(R_T - R_1)$

    (b) 60 Ω

18. $75 = 50 + \dfrac{50 R_2}{50 + R_2} \rightarrow 25(50 + R_2) = 50 R_2 \rightarrow$

    $25 R_2 = 1250 \rightarrow R_2 = 50$ Ω

19. 42 V

20. 2400 W, 600 W

21. $\dfrac{l}{2} + 1.2\left(\dfrac{l}{2}\right) + l = 10 \rightarrow l = 4.8$ ft,

    $0.6l = 2.9$ ft, $\dfrac{l}{2} = 2.4$ ft

22. $(1.5R_3 - 100) + 1.5R_3 + R_3 = 300 \rightarrow R_1 = 50$ Ω, $R_2 = 150$ Ω, $R_3 = 100$ Ω

23. (a) $\Delta I_T = \left(0.30 + \dfrac{V_2}{R_0}\right) - \left(0.30 + \dfrac{V_1}{R_0}\right) \rightarrow$

    $\Delta I_T = \dfrac{\Delta V}{R_0}$

    (b) $\Delta I_T = \dfrac{3}{100} = 0.03$ A $= 30$ mA

24. $\Delta I_T = \dfrac{V_1 + V_{1/3} - V_1}{R_0} \rightarrow \Delta I_T = \dfrac{V_1}{3R_0}$

CHAPTER 12   Series and Parallel DC Circuits

Exercise 12.1   Series Circuits

1. $R_T = 100 + 200 = 300\ \Omega,\ I = \dfrac{24}{300} = 80$ mA,

   $V_1 = (0.08)(100) =\ 8$ V, $V_2 = (0.08)(200) = 16$ V

2. $R_T = 40\ \Omega,\ I = 300$ mA, $V_1 = 3$ V, $V_2 = 9$ V

3. $R_T = \dfrac{120}{2} = 60\ \Omega,\ 2\,R_2 + R_2 = 60 \rightarrow R_1 = 40\ \Omega,$

   $R_2 = 20\ \Omega,\ V_1 = 2.0(40) = 80$ V, $V_2 = 2.0(20) = 40$ V

4. $R_T = 24\ \Omega,\ R_1 = 6\ \Omega,\ R_2 = 18\ \Omega,\ V_1 = 9$ V, $V_2 = 27$ V

5. $V_T = 0.32(3000) = 960$ V, $V_1 + V_1 = 960 \rightarrow$

   $V_1 = V_2 = 480$ V, $R_1 = R_2 = \dfrac{480}{0.32} = 1.5$ kΩ

6. $V_T = 4.1$ V, $V_1 =\ 2.7$ V, $V_2 = 1.4$ V, $R_1 = 3.7$ kΩ, $R_2 = 1.8$ kΩ

7. $I = \dfrac{30}{300} = 100$ mA, $R_1 + 1.5\,R_1 = 30 \rightarrow$

   $R_1 = 120\ \Omega,\ R_2 = 180\ \Omega,\ V_1 = 12$ V, $V_2 = 18$ V

8. $I = 100$ mA, $R_1 = 100\ \Omega,\ R_2 = 200\ \Omega,\ V_1 = 10$ V, $V_2 = 20$ V

9. $I = \dfrac{8}{80} = 100$ mA, $P_1 = (0.1)^2(20) = 200$ mW,

   $P_2 = 240$ mW, $P_3 = 360$ mW, $P_T = 800$ mW

10. $I = 2.0$ A, $P_1 = 60$ W, $P_2 = 72$ W, $P_3 = 88$ W, $P_T = 220$ W

11. $V_T = (0.0009)(8000) = 7.2$ V,
    $P_1 = (0.0009)^2(2000) =\ 1.6$ mW, $P_2 = 2.4$ mW, $P_3 = 2.4$ mW, $P_T = 6.5$ mW

12. $V_T = 20$ V, $P_1 = 300$ mW, $P_2 = 330$ mW, $P_3 = 380$ mW, $P_T = 1.0$ W

13. $V_2 = 4.0$ V, $V_3 = 2(4) = 8.0$ V, $V_T = 16$ V,

    $R_T = \dfrac{16^2}{0.6} = 430\ \Omega$

14. $V_1 = 6.0$ V, $V_2 = 12.0$ V, $V_3 = 6.0$ V, $R_T = 24\ \Omega$

15. $P_1 = 20$ W, $P_2 = 20$ W, $P_3 = 20$ W, $I = 1.4$ A

16. $P_1 = 150$ W, $P_2 = 75$ W, $P_3 = 75$ W, $V_T = 190$ V

17. $240\ \Omega$

18. $48\ \Omega$

19. $I = \sqrt{\dfrac{14}{330}} = 0.206$ A,

    $R_D = R_T - R_L = \dfrac{100}{0.206} - 330 = 160\ \Omega$

20. $48\ \Omega$

21. $V_1 = 15$ V, $V_2 = 30$ V, $P = 27$ W

22. $V_1 + V_1 + 50 = (1.2)(160) \rightarrow V_1 = 71$ V, $V_2 = 121$ V

23. $\Delta V = (1.0)(15) = 15 \rightarrow V_2 = 45$ V or 15 V

24. 10 V or 34 V

25. Total resistance doubles $\rightarrow$ Add 2.7 kΩ

26. Total resistance increases $\left(\dfrac{4}{3}\right)2700 = 3600\ \Omega \rightarrow$

    Need to add 900 Ω

Exercise 12.2   Parallel Circuits

1. $\dfrac{(10)(30)}{10 + 30} = 7.5\ \Omega$

2. $8.0\ \Omega$

3. $230\ \Omega$

4. 1.3 kΩ

5. 28 kΩ

6. $4.1\ \Omega$

7. $12\ \Omega$

8. $2.5\ \Omega$

9. $460\ \Omega$

10. 450 kΩ

11. $\dfrac{(150)(75)}{(150 - 75)} = 150\ \Omega$

12. $20\ \Omega$

13. $30\ \Omega$

14. $150\ \Omega$

15. 1.9 kΩ

16. $510\ \Omega$

17. 1.2 kΩ

18. 1.3 kΩ

19. $G_T = \dfrac{1}{15} + \dfrac{1}{30} + \dfrac{1}{30} \approx 130$ mS, $R_T = \dfrac{1}{G_T} = 7.5\ \Omega$

20. 250 mS, $4.0\ \Omega$

21. 9.1 mS, 110 Ω

22. 590 µs, 1.7 kΩ

23. 170 mS, 6.0 Ω

24. 22 µs, 46 kΩ

25. 11 mS, 94 Ω

26. 79 mS, 13 Ω

27. 2.5 mS, 390 Ω

28. 3.1 µs, 330 kΩ

29. $\dfrac{1}{R_1} = \dfrac{1}{100} - \dfrac{1}{300} - \dfrac{1}{300} \rightarrow R_1 = 300\ \Omega$

30. 24 kΩ

31. 1.0 kΩ

32. 18 Ω

33. 20 Ω

34. 200 Ω

35. 150 Ω

36. 39 Ω

37. $I_1 = \dfrac{12}{24} = 500\ \text{mA},\ I_2 = \dfrac{12}{30} = 400\ \text{mA} \rightarrow$

    $I_T = 900\ \text{mA},\ R_T = \dfrac{12}{0.90} = 13\ \Omega$

38. $I_1 = 160\ \text{mA},\ I_2 = 120\ \text{mA},\ I_T = 280\ \text{mA},\ R_T = 130\ \Omega$

39. $V = \dfrac{P_2}{I_2} = \dfrac{10}{1.0} = 10\ \text{V},\ R_1 = \dfrac{10^2}{20} = 5\ \Omega \rightarrow$

    $R_2 = 10\ \Omega,\ R_T = 3.3\ \Omega,\ I_1 = \dfrac{20}{10} = 2.0\ \text{A},\ I_T = 3.0\ \text{A}$

40. $R_1 = 80\ \Omega,\ R_2 = 40\ \Omega,\ R_T = 27\ \Omega,\ I_1 = 250\ \text{mA},$
    $I_2 = 500\ \text{mA},\ I_T = 750\ \text{mA}$

41. $I_1 = \dfrac{50}{150} = 330\ \text{mA},\ I_2 = \dfrac{50}{200} = 250\ \text{mA},$

    $I_3 = \dfrac{50}{180} = 280\ \text{mA},\ I_T = 860\ \text{mA},\ G_T = 17\ \text{mS},$

    $R_T = 58\ \Omega$

42. $I_1 = 750\ \text{mA},\ I_2 = 630\ \text{mA},\ I_3 = 500\ \text{mA},$
    $I_T = 1.9\ \text{A},\ G_T = 130\ \text{mS},\ R_T = 8.0\ \Omega$

43. $R_1 R_2 = R_T R_2 + R_T R_1 \rightarrow R_1 R_2$
    $\qquad = R_T(R_1 + R_2) \rightarrow$

    $R_T = \dfrac{R_1 R_2}{R_1 + R_2}$

44. $R_T(R_1 + R_2) = R_1 R_2 \rightarrow R_T R_1$
    $+ R_T R_2 = R_1 R_2 \rightarrow R_1(R_2 - R_T)$

    $= R_T R_2 \rightarrow R_1 = \dfrac{R_2 R_T}{R_2 - R_T}$

45. $R_{eq} = \dfrac{(100)(150)}{250} = 60\ \Omega \rightarrow$

    $\dfrac{60}{100} = 60\%,\ \dfrac{60}{150} = 40\%$

46. $R_{eq} = \dfrac{(R_1)(2R_1)}{R_1 + 2R_1} = \dfrac{2R_1^2}{3R_1} = \dfrac{2R_1}{3}$

Exercise 12.3   Series-Parallel Circuits

1. $R_T = 20 + \dfrac{30(15)}{30 + 15} = 30\ \Omega$

2. 170 Ω

3. $R_T = 120 + 130 + \dfrac{300(200)}{300 + 200} = 370\ \Omega$

4. 91 Ω

5. $22 = 12 + \dfrac{15R_3}{15 + R_3} \rightarrow$

    $150 + 10R_3 = 15R_3 \rightarrow R_3 = 30\ \Omega$

6. 30 Ω

7. 13 Ω

8. 10 Ω

9. $R_T = \dfrac{R_1 R_2}{R_1 + R_2} + R_3;\ R_T = 180\ \Omega$

10. $R_T = \dfrac{(R_1 + R_2 + R_3)R_4}{R_1 + R_2 + R_3 + R_4};\ R_T = 33\ \Omega$

11. $I_T = \dfrac{14}{540} = 26\ \text{mA},\ V_2 = 0.026(240) = 6.2\ \text{V},$

    $V_4 = 0.026(100) = 2.6\ \text{V},\ I_4 = \dfrac{2.6}{300} = 8.7\ \text{mA}$

12. $R_T = 18 + 22 + \dfrac{75(150)}{225} = 90\ \Omega,\ I_T = \dfrac{9}{90} = 100\ \text{mA},$

    $V_2 = 0.10(22) = 2.2\ \text{V},\ V_3 = 0.10(50) = 5.0\ \text{V},$

    $I_3 = \dfrac{5.0}{75} = 67\ \text{mA}$

13. $R_T = 120 + \dfrac{(180 + 120)(200)}{180 + 120 + 200} = 240\ \Omega$

14. $15 = 10 + \dfrac{(5 + 5)(R_4)}{5 + 5 + R_4} \rightarrow$

$50 + 5R_4 = 10R_4 \rightarrow R_4 = 10 \ \Omega$

15. $15 = \dfrac{12R_1}{R_1 + 12} + 7.5 \rightarrow 7.5R_1 + 90 = 12R_1 \rightarrow$

$R_1 = 20 \ \Omega$

16. $1.0 = \dfrac{(R_1 + 3.0)(1.2)}{R_1 + 3 + 1.2} \rightarrow$

$R_1 + 4.2 = 1.2R_1 + 3.6 \rightarrow R_1 = 3.0 \ \text{k}\Omega$

17. $R_T = 20 + \dfrac{(10 + 20)(30)}{10 + 20 + 30} + 15 = 50 \ \Omega$

18. $R_T = 120 + \dfrac{(\frac{100}{2})(200)}{250} = 160 \ \Omega$

19. $R_T = 200 + \dfrac{(100)(150)}{250} = 260 \ \Omega \rightarrow$

$I_T = \dfrac{12}{260} = 46 \ \text{mA}, \ V_1 = (0.046)(100) = 4.6 \ \text{V},$

$V_{2,3} = V_T - V_1 - V_5 = 12 - 4.6 - 4.6 = 2.8 \ \text{V} \rightarrow$

$V_2 = \dfrac{2.8}{2} = 1.4 \ \text{V}$

20. $R_T = 43 + \dfrac{120}{3} = 83 \ \Omega \rightarrow I_T = \dfrac{24}{83} = 290 \ \text{mA},$

$V_1 = (0.29)(43) = 12 \ \text{V}, \ V_2 = 24 - 12 = 12 \ \text{V}$

21. $R_{3,4} = \dfrac{15(10)}{25} = 6.0 \ \Omega \rightarrow R_T = \dfrac{30(15 + 6)}{30 + 21}$

$= 12.4 \ \Omega \rightarrow P_T = \dfrac{(6.0)^2}{12.4} = 2.9 \ \text{W}$

22. $R_T = \dfrac{(10)(30 + \frac{20}{2})}{10 + 40} = 8.0 \ \Omega \rightarrow$

$V_T = (1.2)(8.0) = 9.6 \ \text{V}$

Review Exercises

1. $R_T = 51 \ \Omega, I = 470 \ \text{mA}, V_1 = 16 \ \text{V}, V_2 = 8.5 \ \text{V}$

2. $R_T = 20 \ \Omega, R_1 = 12 \ \Omega, R_2 = 8 \ \Omega, V_1 = 6 \ \text{V}, V_2 = 4 \ \text{V}, P_1 = 3 \ \text{W}, P_2 = 2 \ \text{W}, P_T = 5 \ \text{W}$

3. $V_T = 1.1 \ \text{kV}, P_1 = 690 \ \text{W}, P_2 = 1.0 \ \text{kW}, P_3 = 1.1 \ \text{kW}, P_T = 2.8 \ \text{kW}$

4. $2R_1 + 0.5R_1 = 1100 \rightarrow R_1 = R_2 = 440 \ \Omega, R_3 = 220 \ \Omega$

5. (a) $V_B = \dfrac{5.0}{0.8} = 6.25 \ \text{V} \rightarrow V_D = 9.0 - 6.25 = 2.75 \ \text{V} \rightarrow R_D = \dfrac{2.75}{0.8} = 3.4 \ \Omega$

(b) $R_B = \dfrac{5.0}{(0.8)^2} = 7.81 \ \Omega$ and $V_B = \dfrac{6.25}{2} = 3.13 \ \text{V} \rightarrow$

$I = \dfrac{3.13}{7.81} = 0.40 \ \text{A}$ and $V_D = 9.0 - 3.1 = 5.9 \ \text{V} \rightarrow$

$R_D = \dfrac{5.9}{0.40} = 15 \ \Omega$

6. 120 V, 100 V

7. 69 mS, 15 Ω

8. 330 µs, 3.1 kΩ

9. 4 Ω

10. 290 Ω

11. 110 mS, 9.0 Ω

12. 3.1 mS, 320 Ω

13. 110 Ω

14. 450 Ω

15. $R_B = \dfrac{180(270)}{180 + 270} \approx 110 \ \Omega \rightarrow \text{Add } 110 \ \Omega$

16. $R_T = \dfrac{9.1(10)}{19.1} = 4.76 \approx 4.8 \ \Omega, V_B = (0.8)(4.76) = 3.8 \ \text{V}, I_1 = \dfrac{3.8}{9.1} = 420 \ \text{mA}, I_2 = 380 \ \text{mA},$

$P_1 = (3.8)(0.42) = 1.6 \ \text{W}, P_2 = 1.5 \ \text{W}, P_3 = 3.0 \ \text{W}$

17. $I_1 = \dfrac{40}{33} = 1.2 \ \text{A}, I_2 = 590 \ \text{mA}, I_3 = 400 \ \text{mA}, I_T = 2.2 \ \text{A}, R_T = \dfrac{40}{2.2} = 18 \ \Omega, G_T = \dfrac{1}{18} = 55 \ \text{mS}$

18. $P_3 = 70 - 30 = 40 \ \text{W}, R_1 = \dfrac{100^2}{10} = 1.0 \ \text{k}\Omega, R_2 = 500 \ \Omega, R_3 = 250 \ \Omega, R_T = 143 \approx 140 \ \Omega,$

$G_T = 7.0 \ \text{mS}, I_T = \dfrac{100}{143} = 700 \ \text{mA}, I_1 = \dfrac{100}{1000} = 100 \ \text{mA}, I_2 = 200 \ \text{mA}, I_3 = 400 \ \text{mA}$

19. (a) $R_T = \dfrac{(R_1 + R_2)R_3}{R_1 + R_2 + R_3}$

(b) $R_T = \dfrac{250(150)}{400} = 94 \ \Omega$

20. $3 = \dfrac{(3 + 2)R_3}{5 + R_3} \rightarrow 15 + 3R_3 = 5R_3 \rightarrow R_3 = 7.5 \ \text{k}\Omega$

21. $R_{2,3,4} = \dfrac{200}{2} = 100 \ \Omega \rightarrow R_T = \dfrac{100}{2} = 50 \ \Omega, V_1 = V_T = 0.5(50) = 25 \ \text{V},$

$I_{3,4} = \dfrac{25}{200} = 0.125 \ \text{A} \rightarrow V_3 = 0.125(110) = 14 \ \text{V}, P_T = 0.5(25) = 13 \ \text{W}$

22. $I_1 = \dfrac{6.5}{15} = 430 \ \text{mA}, I_2 = 130 \ \text{mA}, I_3 = \dfrac{6.5}{50 + 75} = 52 \ \text{mA} \rightarrow$

$V_3 = 0.052(50) = 2.6 \ \text{V}, P_T = 6.5(0.43 + 0.13 + 0.052) = 4.0 \ \text{W}$

23. (a) $R_T = R_1 + \dfrac{R_4(R_2 + R_3)}{R_2 + R_3 + R_4}$

(b) $R_T = 240 + \dfrac{1300(1100 + 1600)}{4000} = 1.1 \ \text{k}\Omega, V_T = (0.035)(1100) = 39 \ \text{V}, V_1 = (0.035)(240) = 8.4 \ \text{V}$

24. $R_T = 100 + \dfrac{200(100 + 200)}{500} = 220 \ \Omega, I_T = I_1 = \dfrac{50}{220} = 230 \ \text{mA}$

25. $\dfrac{1}{R_T} = \dfrac{2}{R_1} + \dfrac{1}{2R_1} = \dfrac{5}{2R_1} \rightarrow R_T = \dfrac{2R_1}{5}$

26. $\dfrac{1}{R_T} = \dfrac{2}{R_1} + \dfrac{1}{R_2} \rightarrow R_1 R_2 = 2R_2 R_T + R_1 R_T \rightarrow (R_1 + 2R_2)R_T = R_1 R_2 \rightarrow R_T = \dfrac{R_1 R_2}{R_1 + 2R_2}$

CHAPTER 13 Graphs

Exercise 13.1   Rectangular Coordinate System

1. through 16.

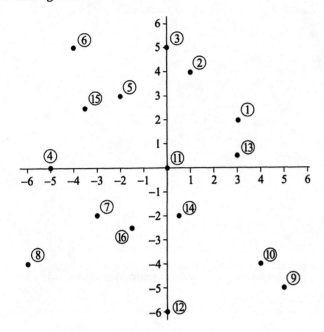

17. $x - y = 3$

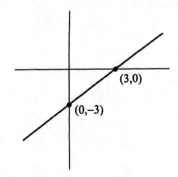

18. $x + y = -5$

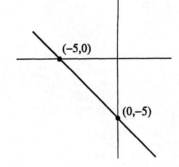

19. $x - 2y = 4$

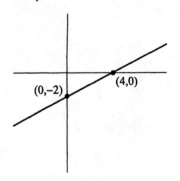

20. $2x + y = -2$

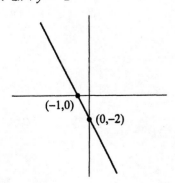

21. $x + y = 0$

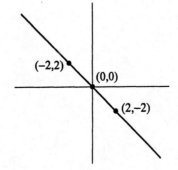

22. $x - 2y = 0$

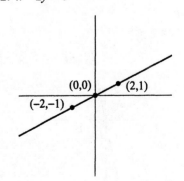

23. $3x + y = 6$

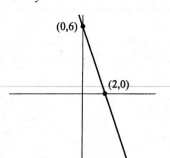

24. $x - 3y = 3$

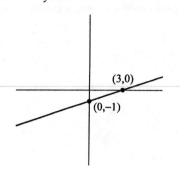

25. $x + 2y = 3$

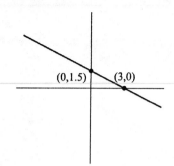

26. $3x - 2y = 3$

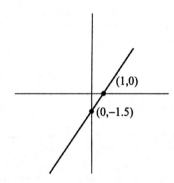

27. $2a + b = 4$

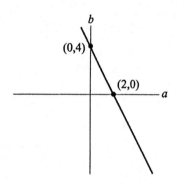

28. $3a - 4b = 12$

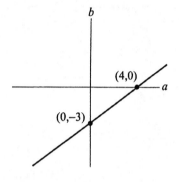

29. $I = \dfrac{V}{10}$

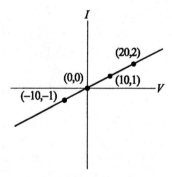

30. $I = \dfrac{V}{150}$

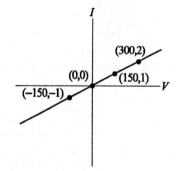

31. $P - 20I = 0$

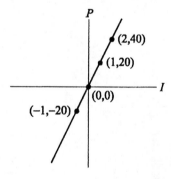

32. $P - 5I = 0$

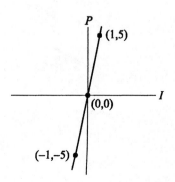

33. $2V_1 + V_2 = 5$

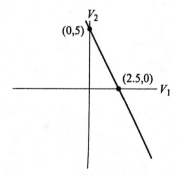

34. $3I_1 - 4I_2 = 6$

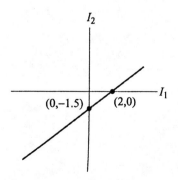

35. $I = \dfrac{V}{12\ V}$

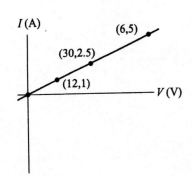

36. $I = \dfrac{V}{1.5\ k\Omega}$

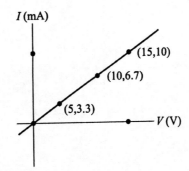

37. $P = 120I$

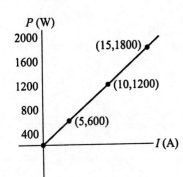

38. $P = 20I$

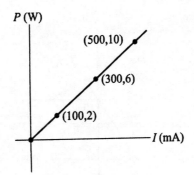

Exercise 13.2   Linear Function

1. $y = x$

$m = 1, b = 0$

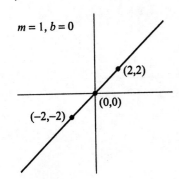

2. $y = 3x$

$m = 3, b = 0$

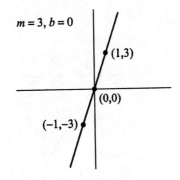

3. $y = 2x - 2$

$m = 2, b = -2$

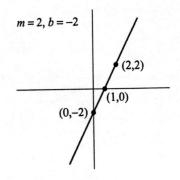

4. $y = x - 3$

$m = 1, b = -3$

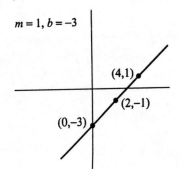

5. $y = -2x - 2$

$m = -2, b = -2$

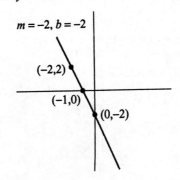

6. $y = -x + 1$

$m = -1, b = 1$

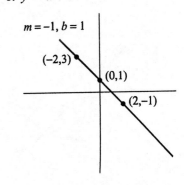

7. $y = -x - 4$

$m = -1, b = -4$

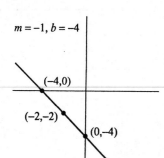

8. $y = -3x + 2$

$m = -3, b = 2$

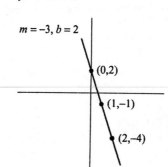

9. $y = 3x - 4$

$m = 3, b = -4$

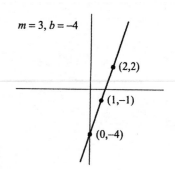

10. $y = 3x + 1$

$m = 3, b = 1$

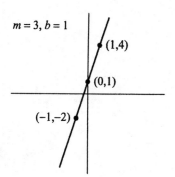

11. $y = \frac{3}{2}x$

$m = \frac{3}{2}, b = 0$

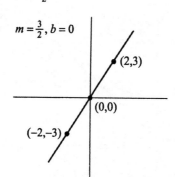

12. $y = \frac{1}{2}x$

$m = \frac{1}{2}, b = 0$

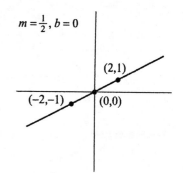

13. $y = -\frac{1}{2}x$

$m = -\frac{1}{2}, b = 0$

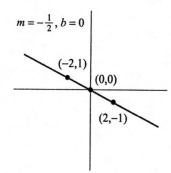

14. $y = -\frac{3}{2}x$

$m = -\frac{3}{2}, b = 0$

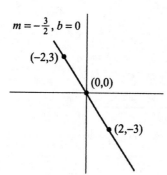

15. $y = x + \frac{3}{2}$

$m = 1, b = \frac{3}{2}$

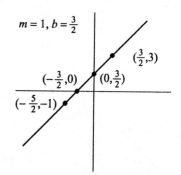

16. $y = -x + \frac{5}{2}$

$m = -1, b = \frac{5}{2}$

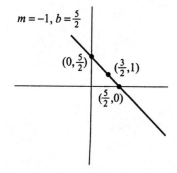

17. $P = 3.5I$

$m = 3.5, b = 0$

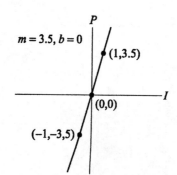

18. $I = 0.10V$

$m = 0.10, b = 0$

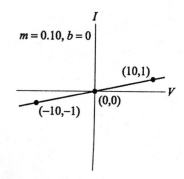

19. $V = 3.2R + 2.3$

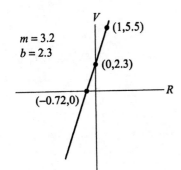

$m = 3.2$
$b = 2.3$

20. $Z = 5.5X - 1.5$

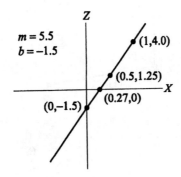

$m = 5.5$
$b = -1.5$

21. $R = -1.6t + 5.0$

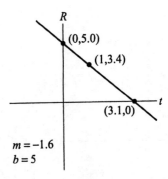

$m = -1.6$
$b = 5$

22. $Q = -0.4t - 1.0$

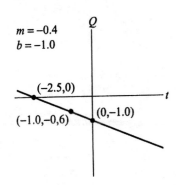

$m = -0.4$
$b = -1.0$

23. $I_2 = 0.5I_1 + 1$

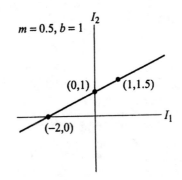

$m = 0.5, b = 1$

24. $E_2 = 20E_1 - 10$

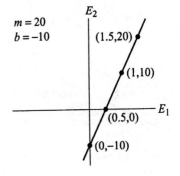

$m = 20$
$b = -10$

25. $v = 100 + 50t$

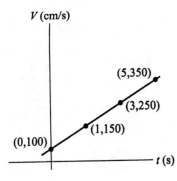

26. $v = 0.607t + 332$

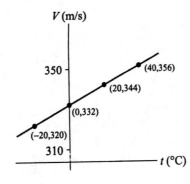

27. (a)

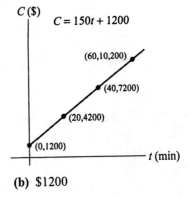

$C = 150t + 1200$

(b) $1200

28. (a)

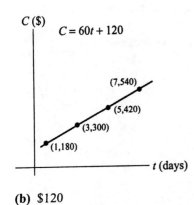

$C = 60t + 120$

(b) $120

29. Slope $= \dfrac{1}{R} = 0.0067$

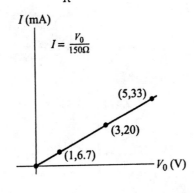

$I = \dfrac{V_0}{150\Omega}$

30. $P = 150I^2$

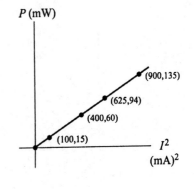

31.

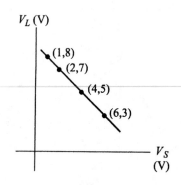

32.

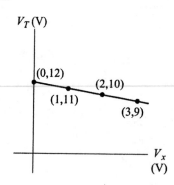

33. $R_t = 0.03t + 15$

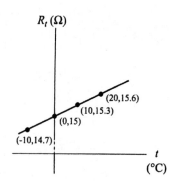

34. $R = \dfrac{\rho l}{A} = \dfrac{10l}{1000l} = \dfrac{l}{100}\ (\Omega) = 10l\ (\text{m}\Omega)$

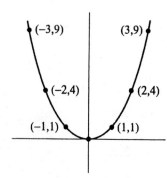

Exercise 13.3   Nonlinear Graphs

1. $y = x^2$

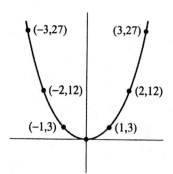

2. $y = 3x^2$

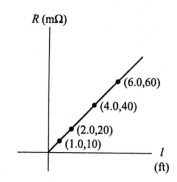

3. $y = 0.5x^2$

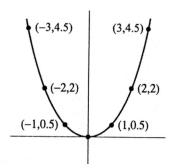

4. $y = 0.8x^2$

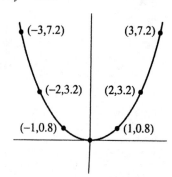

5. $y = 1.2x^2$

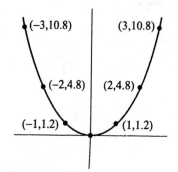

6. $y = 2.5x^2$

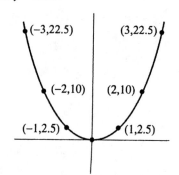

7. $y = -2x^2$

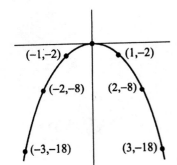

(−1,−2)   (1,−2)
(−2,−8)   (2,−8)
(−3,−18)   (3,−18)

8. $y = -x^2$

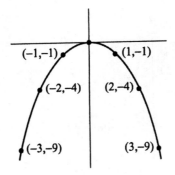

(−1,−1)   (1,−1)
(−2,−4)   (2,−4)
(−3,−9)   (3,−9)

9. $y = -0.6x^2$

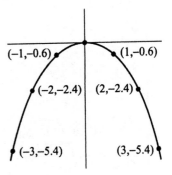

(−1,−0.6)   (1,−0.6)
(−2,−2.4)   (2,−2.4)
(−3,−5.4)   (3,−5.4)

10. $y = -1.5x^2$

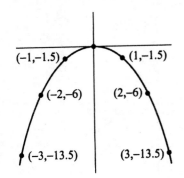

(−1,−1.5)   (1,−1.5)
(−2,−6)   (2,−6)
(−3,−13.5)   (3,−13.5)

11. $P = 10I^2$

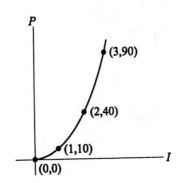

(3,90)
(2,40)
(1,10)
(0,0)

12. $P = 20I^2$

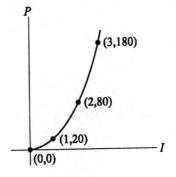

(3,180)
(2,80)
(1,20)
(0,0)

13. $P = 75I^2$

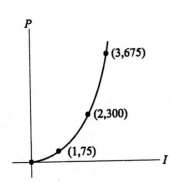

(3,675)
(2,300)
(1,75)

14. $P = 330I^2$

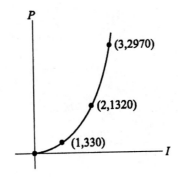

(3,2970)
(2,1320)
(1,330)

15. $P = 0.1V^2$

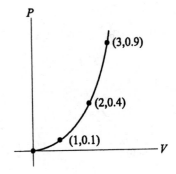

(3,0.9)
(2,0.4)
(1,0.1)

16. $P = 0.02V^2$

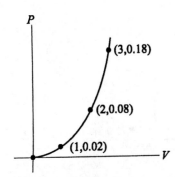

(3,0.18)
(2,0.08)
(1,0.02)

17. $I = \dfrac{12}{R}$

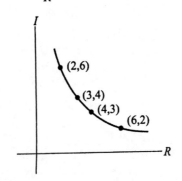

(2,6)
(3,4)
(4,3)
(6,2)

18. $I = \dfrac{36}{R}$

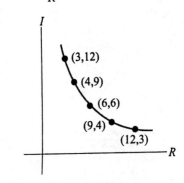

(3,12)
(4,9)
(6,6)
(9,4)
(12,3)

19. $I = \dfrac{220}{R}$

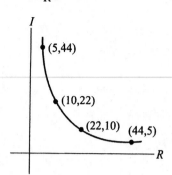

20. $I = \dfrac{60}{R}$

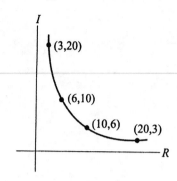

21. $I = \dfrac{9.2}{R}$

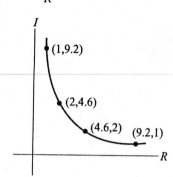

22. $I = \dfrac{12.6}{R}$

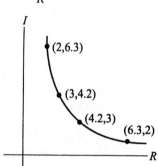

23. $I = \dfrac{5.5}{V}$

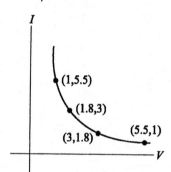

24. $I = \dfrac{40}{V}$

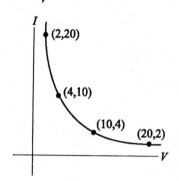

25. $d = 16t^2$

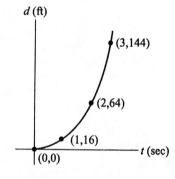

26. $h = 0.001x^2$

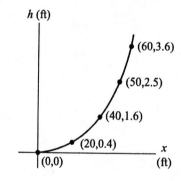

27. $P = 22I^2$

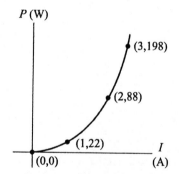

28. $P = 680I^2$

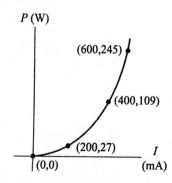

29. $P = \dfrac{V^2}{200}$

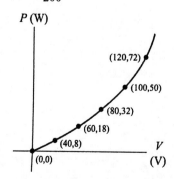

30. $P = \dfrac{V^2}{1.2}$

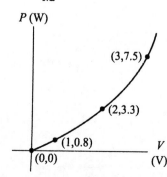

31. $IR = 9.0$

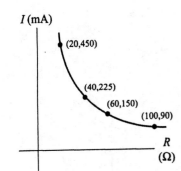

32. $IR = 220$

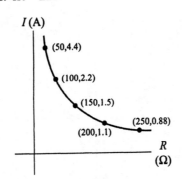

33. $PR = 6400$

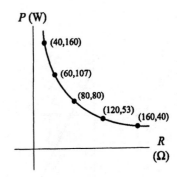

34. $PR = 6.25$

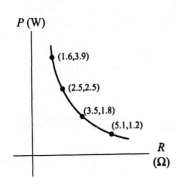

35. (a)

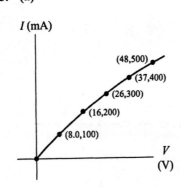

(b) $80\ \Omega, 80\ \Omega, 87\ \Omega, 93\ \Omega, 96\ \Omega$

36. (a)

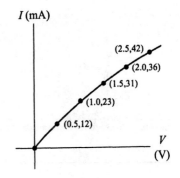

(b) $42\ \Omega, 43\ \Omega, 48\ \Omega, 56\ \Omega, 60\ \Omega$

37. (a)

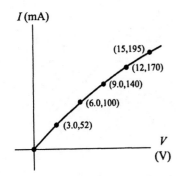

(b) $58\ \Omega, 60\ \Omega, 64\ \Omega, 71\ \Omega, 77\ \Omega$

38. (a)

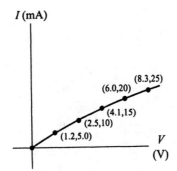

(b) $240\ \Omega, 250\ \Omega, 273\ \Omega, 300\ \Omega, 332\ \Omega$

39.

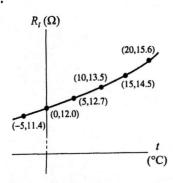

40.

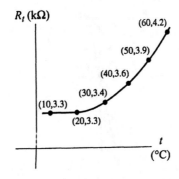

Review Exercises

1. $2x + y = 2$

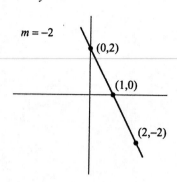

$m = -2$
(0,2)
(1,0)
(2,-2)

2. $3x - y = 6$

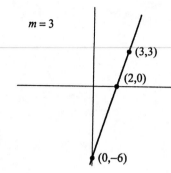

$m = 3$
(3,3)
(2,0)
(0,-6)

3. $2x - 5y = 5$

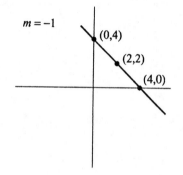

$m = \frac{2}{5}$
$(\frac{5}{2},0)$
(5,1)
(0,-1)

4. $4x + y = 8$

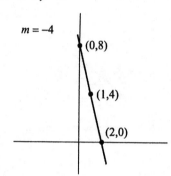

$m = -4$
(0,8)
(1,4)
(2,0)

5. $y = 2x - 5$

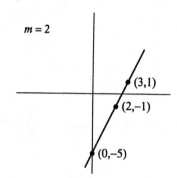

$m = 2$
(3,1)
(2,-1)
(0,-5)

6. $y = -x + 4$

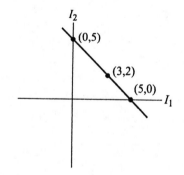

$m = -1$
(0,4)
(2,2)
(4,0)

7. $5x + 2y = 0$

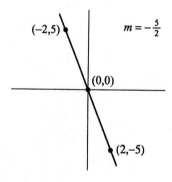

(-2,5)
$m = -\frac{5}{2}$
(0,0)
(2,-5)

8. $2x - 2y = 3$

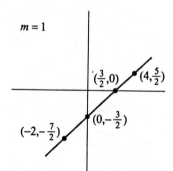

$m = 1$
$(\frac{3}{2},0)$
$(4,\frac{5}{2})$
$(0,-\frac{3}{2})$
$(-2,-\frac{7}{2})$

9. $I_1 + I_2 = 5$

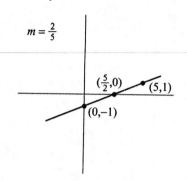

I_2
(0,5)
(3,2)
(5,0)
I_1

10. $V_1 - 2V_2 = 4$

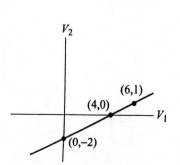

V_2
(6,1)
(4,0)
V_1
(0,-2)

11. $P - 10V = 0$

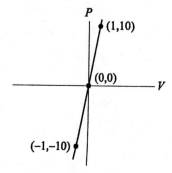

P
(1,10)
(0,0)
V
(-1,-10)

12. $I = 0.04V$

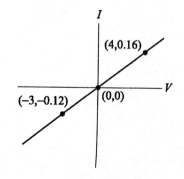

I
(4,0.16)
(-3,-0.12)
(0,0)
V

13. $P_T = 9.4I$

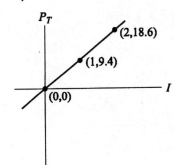

14. $E = 120 - 100d$

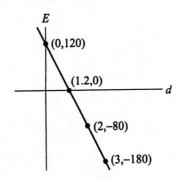

15. $V = 1.6R + 3.2$

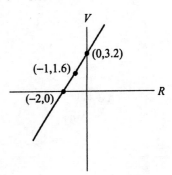

16. $R = 0.023t + 0.05$

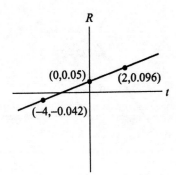

17. $y = 1.5x^2$

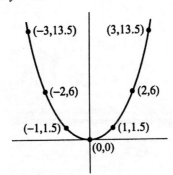

18. $y = 4x^2$

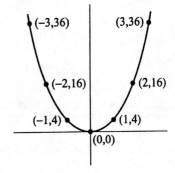

19. $y = -3x^2$

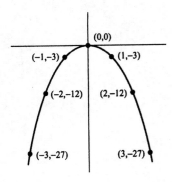

20. $y = 0.8x^2$

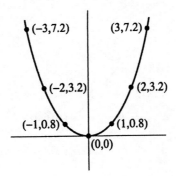

21. $P = 12I^2$

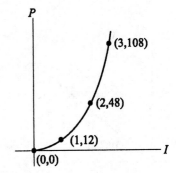

22. $P = 0.5V^2$

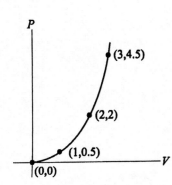

23. $I = \dfrac{28}{R}$

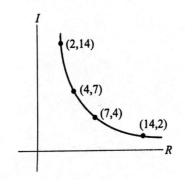

24. $I = \dfrac{6.4}{R}$

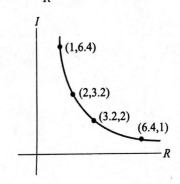

25. $I = \dfrac{60}{V}$

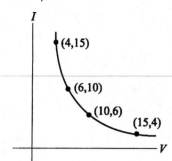

26. $R = \dfrac{3.2}{I}$

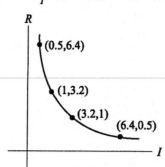

27. $F = 1.5x$

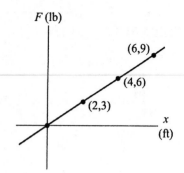

28. $W = 0.97H - 100$

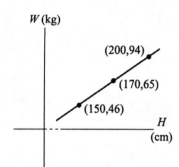

29. $C = 2\pi r$

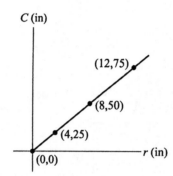

30. (a)

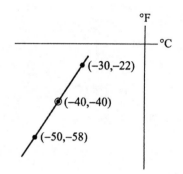

(b) $C = 1.8C + 32 \rightarrow 0.8C$
$= -32 \rightarrow C = -40$

31. $I = \dfrac{V}{36 \text{ k}\Omega}$

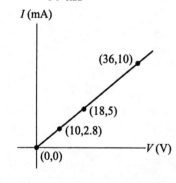

32. $V_C = 16 - V_L$

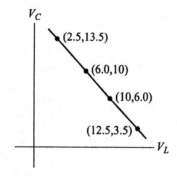

33. $Q = 2.76 + 1.22t$

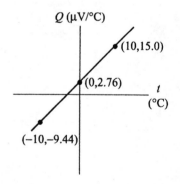

34. $P_T = 60I_T$

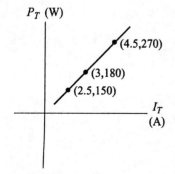

35. $P = 120I^2$

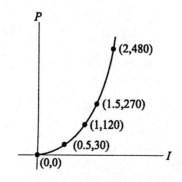

36. $IR = 12$

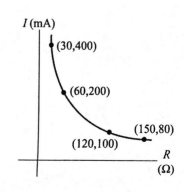

37. (a)

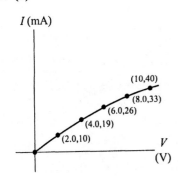

(b) 200 Ω, 211 Ω, 231 Ω, 242 Ω, 250 Ω

38.

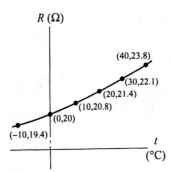

CHAPTER 14   Linear Systems

Exercise 14.1   Graphical Solution of Two Equations

1.

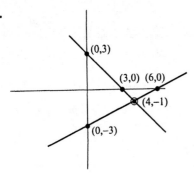

2.

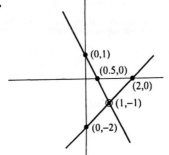

3.

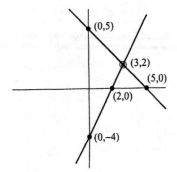

4.

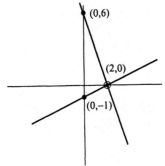

5.

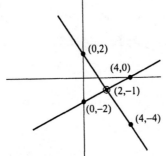

6.

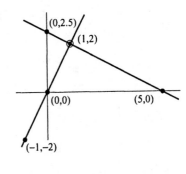

7.

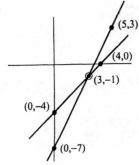

8.

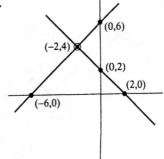

9.

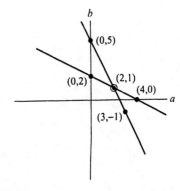

10.

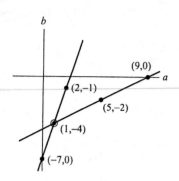

11.

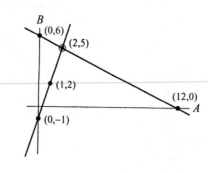

12.

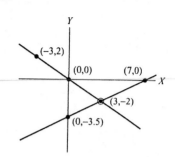

13.

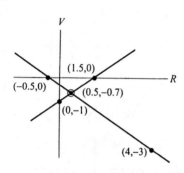

14.

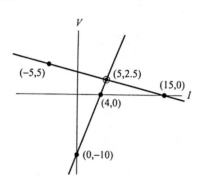

15.

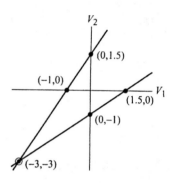

16.

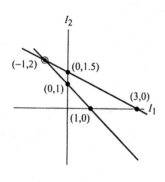

17.

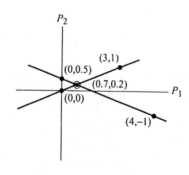

18.

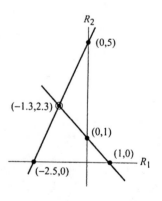

19.

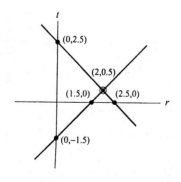

20.

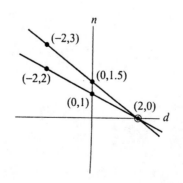

21.

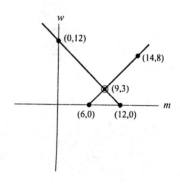

22.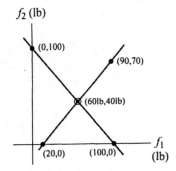

23.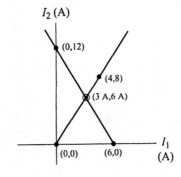

24.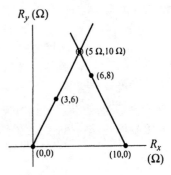

25. $V_1 + V_2 = 20$
$V_1 - V_2 = 10$

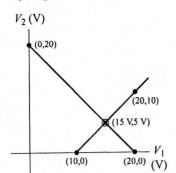

26. $V_1 + V_2 = 8$
$V_1 - V_2 = 2$

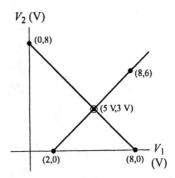

Exercise 14.2   Algebraic Solution of Two Equations

1. $(4,-1)$

2. $(1,-1)$

3. $(3,2)$

4. $(2,0)$

5. $(2,-1)$

6. $(1,2)$

7. $(3,-1)$

8. $(-2,4)$

9. $(2,1)$

10. $(1,-4)$

11. $(2,5)$

12. $(3,-2)$

13. $(-0.67,0.5)$

14. $(5,2.5)$

15. $(-3,-3)$

16. $(-1,2)$

17. $(0.71,0.24)$

18. $(-1.3,2.3)$

19. $(1.9,-0.23)$

20. $(-0.67,3.3)$

21. $(-2.8,-3.2)$

22. $(0.25,1.5)$

23. $(-2.4,5.2)$

24. $(0.4,0.8)$

25. $2l + 2w = 108$, $w = \dfrac{l}{2} \rightarrow w = 18$ m $= 59$ ft,

$l = 36$ m $= 120$ ft

26. $2l + 3w = 105$, $l = 2w \rightarrow w = 15$ ft $= 4.6$ m,

$l = 30$ ft $= 9.1$ m

27. $M_R + M_S = 500$,
$0.0125(M_R) + 0.015(M_S) = 6.75 \rightarrow M_R = \$300$,
$M_S = \$200$

28. $A + B = 1000$,
$0.055A + 0.045B = 50.5 \rightarrow A = \$550$,
$B = \$450$

29. $t_u + t_d = 5$, $t_u = 2t_d \rightarrow t_u = 3.3$ h, $t_d = 1.7$ h

30. $t_w + t_r = 1$, $4t_w + 20t_r = 16 \rightarrow t_w = \dfrac{1}{4}$ h $= 15$ min,

$t_r = \dfrac{3}{4}$, h $= 45$ min

31. $100\ \Omega$, $200\ \Omega$

32. 5.5 A, 3.5 A

33. 22 V, 12 V

34. 6.0 V, 20 Ω

35. 110 mA, 740 mA

36. $I_A = 190$ mA, $I_B = 74$ mA

37. **(a)** $G_1 + G_2 = 90$,
$\quad G_1 + G_2 + 2G_2 = 190 \rightarrow G_1 = 40$ mS,
$\quad G_2 = 50$ mS
(b) $R_1 = 25$ Ω, $R_2 = 20$ Ω

38. $1200 = 400 + L_2 + L_M$,
$\quad 500 = 400 + L_2 - L_M \rightarrow L_2 = 450$ μH,
$\quad L_M = 350$ μH

39. $5t_1 + 9t_2 = 60$,
$\quad 7t_1 + 12t_2 = 81 \rightarrow t_1 = 3$ ns,
$\quad t_2 = 5$ ns

40. $0.25(R_X + 10) = V_B$,
$\quad 0.20(R_X + 20) = V_B \rightarrow R_x = 30$ Ω,
$\quad V_B = 10$ V

41. $0.10(R_X + R_Y) = 12$,
$\quad 0.06(2R_X + R_Y) = 12 \rightarrow R_x = 80$ Ω,
$\quad R_y = 40$ Ω

42. $R_x = 150$ Ω, $R_y = 100$ Ω

Exercise 14.3   Solution by Determinants

1. 5

2. 14

3. 21

4. $\frac{1}{2}$

5. −7.8

6. 0.33

7. (2,5)

8. (3,−2)

9. (−0.4,0.5)

10. (5,2.5)

11. (3,1)

12. (0,2)

13. (−0.5,0.33)

14. (1,2.5)

15. (−2.8,−3.2)

16. (0.25,1.5)

17. (−3,−3)

18. (−1,2)

19. (0.71,0.24)

20. (−1.3,2.3)

21. (−2,−4)

22. (−3,2)

23. (0.6,0.4)

24. (1.8,−0.8)

25. (1.3,1.1)

26. (1.6,3.2)

27. (−2.2,−4.4)

28. (0.2,0.8)

29. (−2.4,5.2)

30. (0.4,0.8)

31. (1.9,−0.23)

32. (−0.67,3.3)

33. 1000, 1500

34. $x + y = 650$,
$\quad 1.5x + 1.7y = 1045 \rightarrow x = 300$,
$\quad y = 350$

35. $t_u + t_d = 4$,
$\quad t_u = 2t_d \rightarrow t_d = 1.3$ h,
$\quad t_u = 2.7$ h

36. $\left(\dfrac{21}{60}\right)R_C + \left(\dfrac{6}{60}\right)R_D = 10$, $\left(\dfrac{9}{60}\right)R_C + \left(\dfrac{14}{60}\right)R_D$
$\quad = 10 \rightarrow R_C = 20$ mi/h, $R_D = 30$ mi/h

37. 190 mA, 100 mA

38. 15×10^{-6} N, 13×10^{-6} N

39. 32 V, 24 V

40. 3.0 A, 1.5 A

41. $23.3 = 50a + R_0$, $27.1 = 100a + R_0 \rightarrow$
$\quad R_0 = 19.5 \approx 20$ Ω, $a = 0.76$, $\alpha = \dfrac{a}{R_0} = 0.0039/°$ C

42. $90 = 20a + R_0$, $84 = 80a + R_0 \rightarrow$
$\quad R_0 = 92$ Ω, $a = -0.10/°$C, $\alpha = -0.0011/°$C

Exercise 14.4   Solution of Three Linear Equations

1. 2

2. −53

3. −56

4. 1

5. 13

6. −65

7. (1, 2, 3)

8. (2, −3, 1)

9. (4, −1, 3)

10. (−3, 2, 4)

11. (0.1, 0.5, −0.3)

12. (0.5, 0.33, 0.17)

13. (3, −5, −1)

14. (3, 4, 2)

15. (0.5, 0.67, 0.6)

16. (2.0, 1.0, 1.5)

17. (0.5, 1.0, −0.5)

18. (0.33, 0.66, 0.11)

19. $a + b = 1$, $a − b + c = 0$, $3a − b = 0 \rightarrow a = 0.25$ gal, $b = 0.75$ gal, $c = 0.50$ gal

20. $P_1 + P_2 + P_3 = 600$, $P_1 + P_2 = 300$, $P_1 + P_3 = 400 \rightarrow P_1 = 100$ gal/h, $P_2 = 200$ gal/h, $P_3 = 300$ gal/h

21. 50 V, 200 V, 150 V

22. (0.2, −0.3, 0.3)

23. 720 mA, 880 mA, 160 mA

24. 13 mA, 17 mA, 3 mA

25. 1.8 A, 1.1 A, 1.6 A

26. 1.9 A, 1.2 A, 1.6 A, 1.6 A

Review Exercises

1.

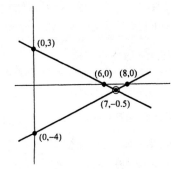

2.

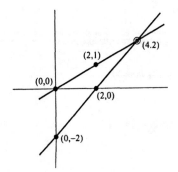

3.

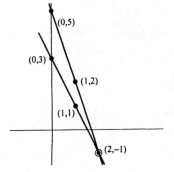

4.

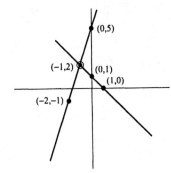

5.

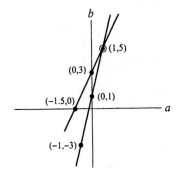

6.

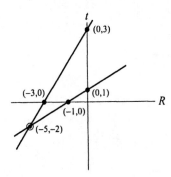

7.

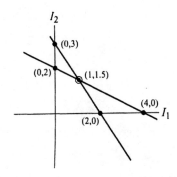

8.

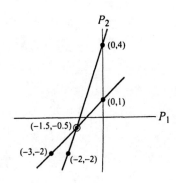

9.

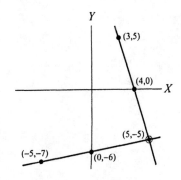

10.

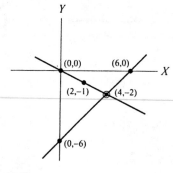

11. (4,1)

12. (3,1)

13. (2,–1)

14. (–1,2)

15. (7,2)

16. (7,4)

17. (2,0)

18. (–1,1)

19. (5,–3)

20. (4,–1)

21. (0.4,0.9)

22. (0.75,–1.3)

23. –28

24. 15

25. –0.44

26. –5.8

27. 0

28. –1.0

29. 250

30. –5.1

31. (3,0.33)

32. (2,–2)

33. (2,0.5)

34. (–1.5,–0.5)

35. (0.4,0.9)

36. (0.75,–1.3)

37. (2.5,3.5)

38. (0.50,0.75)

39. (10,–8)

40. (4,–4)

41. (3,–2)

42. (1.6,–9)

43. (2, –1, 3)

44. (2, –1, –1)

45. (1.5, 1, 0.5)

46. (1.2, 0.2, –1.6)

47. (3, –1, 1)

48. (0.5, 2, 0)

49. (1.5, 2, 3.5)

50. $I = 3, R = 2, V = 2.5$

51. $l = 1.5w,$
$2l + 2w = 155 \rightarrow w = 31$ m,
$l = 46.5$ m

52. $A + B = 1000,$
$0.05A + 0.06B = 54 \rightarrow A = \$600,$
$B = \$400$

53. $S + C = 11,700,$
$S + C + F = 12,800,$
$F - 5.5C = 0 \rightarrow S = \$11,500$

54. $4p + 2s = 26,$
$6(p + s) = 74 - 26 = 48 \rightarrow p = 5$ mi/h,
$s = 3$ mi/h

55. $V_1 + V_2 = 2.5(10), V_1 - V_2 = 1.5(10) \rightarrow$
$V_1 = 20$ V, $V_2 = 5$ V

56. $G_1 + G_2 = 100, \dfrac{G_1}{2} + G_2 = 60 \rightarrow$
$G_1 = 80$ mS, $G_2 = 20$ mS,
$R_1 = 12.5$ Ω, $R_2 = 50$ Ω

57. $G_1 + G_2 = 28, 2G_1 + G_2 = 38 \rightarrow$
$G_1 = 10$ mS, $G_2 = 18$ mS, $R_1 = 100$ Ω,
$R_2 = 56$ Ω

58. $1.88(r + 3.0) = V,$
$1.15(r + 5.1) = V \rightarrow 6.2$ V,
310 mΩ

59. 0.60, 0.40, 0.20

60. $0.010(R_1 + R_2 + R_3) = 6,$
$0.020(R_1 + R_2) = 6,$
$0.015(R_2 + R_3) = 6 \rightarrow R_1 = 200$ Ω,
$R_2 = 300$ Ω, $R_3 = 100$ Ω

61. 200 mA, 100 mA

62. 157 mA, 57 mA, 214 mA

CHAPTER 15 Network Analysis

Exercise 15.1 Voltage Division

1. $V_1 = \left(\dfrac{25}{70}\right)(9.0) = 3.2$ V, $V_2 = 1.9$ V, $V_3 = 3.9$ V

2. 7.7 V, 19 V, 5.1 V

3. $V_1 = 12$ V, $V_2 = \left(\dfrac{400}{400 + 200}\right)(12) = 8.0$ V, $V_3 = 4.0$ V

4. 200 V, 50 V, 150 V

5. $R_T = 10 + \dfrac{10(15)}{25} = 16$ Ω, $I_T = \dfrac{24}{16} = 1.5$ A,

$V_4 = 1.5(10) = 15$ V, $V_1 = 24 - 15 = 9.0$ V,

$I_1 = \dfrac{9}{10} = 900$ mA, $I_2 = 1500 - 900 = 600$ mA,

$V_2 = V_3 = 4.5$ V

6. $R_T = 30$ Ω, $I_T = 2.0$ A, $V_4 = 30$ V, $V_1 = 30$ V, $I_1 = 1.0$ A, $I_2 = 1.0$ A, $V_2 = 10$ V, $V_3 = 20$ V

7. $\dfrac{1}{R_T} = \dfrac{1}{10} + \dfrac{1}{20} + \dfrac{1}{5} \rightarrow R_T = 2.9$ kΩ,

$I_T = \dfrac{200}{2.9} = 70$ mA, $I_1 = \dfrac{200}{10} = 20$ mA,

$I_2 = 10$ mA, $I_4 = 40$ mA, $V_1 = V_2 = 200$ V,

$V_3 = \left(\dfrac{2}{5}\right)(200) = 80$ V, $V_4 = 120$ V

8. 5.5 Ω, 270 mA, 130 mA, 100 mA, 50 mA, 1.5 V, 1.5 V, 1.0 V, 0.5 V

9. $\dfrac{R_2}{100 + R_2} = 0.20 \rightarrow R_2 = 25$ Ω

10. $\dfrac{R_2}{120 + R_2} = \dfrac{1}{4} \rightarrow R_2 = 40$ Ω

11. $12 = \dfrac{R_1}{R_1 + 2R_1}(V_{1,2}) = \left(\dfrac{1}{3}\right)V_{1,2} \rightarrow V_{1,2} = 36$ V $\rightarrow$

$V_2 = 24$ V, $V_3 = \left(\dfrac{R_3}{R_3 + 3R_3}\right)(36) = 9$ V, $V_4 = 27$ V

12. $20 = \dfrac{R_1}{R_1 + 0.5R_1}(V_{1,2}) \rightarrow V_{1,2} = 30$ V $\rightarrow$

$V_2 = 10$ V, $V_3 = 24$ V, $V_4 = 6$ V

Exercise 15.2 Kirchhoff's Laws

1. The algebraic sum of all currents entering and leaving any branch point in a circuit equals zero.

2. The algebraic sum of the voltages around any closed path equals zero.

3. $I_1 - I_2 - I_3 = 0$

4. $I_2 + I_3 - I_1 = 0$

5. $V_0 - I_1R_1 - I_2R_2 = 0$

6. $V_0 - I_1R_1 - I_3R_3 = 0$

7. $I_2R_2 - I_3R_3 = 0$

8. $I_3 - I_1 - I_2 = 0$

9. $I_1 + I_2 - I_3 = 0$

10. $V_1 - V_2 + I_2R_2 - I_1R_1 = 0$

11. $V_1 - I_3R_3 - I_1R_1 = 0$

12. $V_2 - I_3R_3 - I_2R_2 = 0$

13. $I_1 - I_2 - I_3 + I_4 = 0$

14. $I_2 + I_3 - I_1 - I_4 = 0$

15. $V_1 - I_1R_1 - V_2 + I_4R_4 = 0$

16. $V_1 - I_1R_1 - I_2R_2 = 0$

17. $V_2 - I_3R_3 - I_4R_4 = 0$

18. $I_2R_2 - I_3R_3 = 0$

Exercise 15.3 Solving Circuits

1. $I_1 - I_2 - I_3 = 0$, $3I_1 + 10I_2 = 8$, $3I_1 + 10I_3 = 8 \rightarrow I_1 = 1.0$ A, $I_2 = 500$ mA, $I_3 = 500$ mA

2. 500 mA, 300 mA, 200 mA

3. 280 mA, 190 mA, 90 mA

4. 45 mA, 27 mA, 18 mA

5. $-I_1 - I_2 + I_3 = 0$, $20I_1 + 10I_3 = 10$, $10I_2 + 10I_3 = 15 \rightarrow I_1 = 100$ mA, $I_2 = 700$ mA, $I_3 = 800$ mA

6. 1.4 A, 630 mA, 2.0 A

7. 100 mA, 300 mA, 400 mA

8. 21 mA, 7.5 mA, 29 mA

9. At junction of R_1, R_2 and R_3: $I_1 - I_2 + I_3 = 0$, $4I_1 - 3I_3 = 6$, $6I_2 + 3I_3 = 12 \rightarrow I_1 = 1.7$ A, $I_2 = 1.9$ A, $I_3 = 230$ mA

10. 1.4 A, 1.0 A, 400 mA

11. Apply Kirchhoff's laws: $V_X = 0.20R_X + (0.20)(10)$, $V_X = 0.10R_X + (0.10)(30) \rightarrow V_X = 4.0$ V, $R_X = 10\ \Omega$

12. Apply Kirchhoff's laws: $V_X = 300I_X$, $V_X + 20 = 1300I_X \rightarrow V_X = 6.0$ V, $I_X = 20$ mA

13. Replace bank of R_2 and R_3 with $R_{2,3} = 10\ \Omega$. Then at junction of R_1 and $R_{2,3}$: $I_1 - I_{2,3} + I_4 = 0$, $10I_1 + 10I_{2,3} = 12$ and $10I_{2,3} + I_4 = 18 \rightarrow I_1 = 200$ mA, $I_2 = I_3 = 500$ mA, $I_4 = 800$ mA

14. 2.0 mA, 3.5 mA, 3.5 mA, 5.0 mA

Review Exercises

1. $V_1 = 26$ V, $V_2 = \left(\dfrac{30}{130}\right)26 = 6.0$ V, $V_3 = 8.0$ V, $V_4 = 12$ V

2. $V_1 = V_2 = 100$ V, $V_3 = \left(\dfrac{400}{600}\right)100 = 67$ V, $V_4 = 33$ V

3. $R_T = \dfrac{100(130)}{230} = 57\ \Omega$, $I_T = \dfrac{13}{57} = 230$ mA, $V_1 = 13$ V, $V_2 = \left(\dfrac{30}{130}\right)13 = 3.0$ V, $V_3 = 4.0$ V, $V_4 = 6.0$ V, $I_1 = \dfrac{13}{100} = 130$ mA, $I_2 = I_3 = I_4 = \dfrac{13}{130} = 100$ mA

4. $\dfrac{1}{R_T} = \dfrac{1}{2000} + \dfrac{1}{1000} + \dfrac{1}{600} \rightarrow R_T = 320\ \Omega$, $V_1 = V_2 = 60$ V, $V_3 = \left(\dfrac{400}{600}\right)60 = 40$ V, $V_4 = 20$ V, $I_1 = \dfrac{60}{2000} = 30$ mA, $I_2 = 60$ mA, $I_3 = I_4 = 100$ mA

5. **X**: $I_1 + I_3 - I_2 = 0 \leftrightarrow$ **Y**: $I_2 - I_1 - I_3 = 0$

6. $V_1 - I_1R_1 - I_2R_2 = 0$, $V_2 - I_3R_3 - I_2R_2 = 0$, $V_1 - I_1R_1 + I_3R_3 - V_2 = 0$

7. At **X**: $I_1 - I_2 + I_3 = 0$, $2I_1 + 4I_2 = 6$, $4I_2 + 2I_3 = 6 \rightarrow I_1 = 600$ mA, $I_2 = 1.2$ A, $I_3 = 600$ mA

8. 103 mA, 28 mA, 131 mA

9. At junction of R_1 and R_3:
$I_1 + I_2 - I_3 = 0$, $50I_1 + 70I_3 = 50$,
$60I_2 + 70I_3 = 100 \rightarrow I_1 = 280$ mA,
$I_2 = 240$ mA, $I_3 = 520$ mA, $V_1 = 0.28(50) = 14$ V,
$V_2 = 24$ V, $V_3 = 36$ V

10. At junction of R_1, R_2, and R_3: $-I_1 - I_2 + I_3 = 0$,
and using R in kΩ and I in mA: $4I_1 + 5I_3 = 220$
and $3I_2 + 5I_3 = 240 \rightarrow I_1 = 12$ mA, $I_2 = 23$ mA,
$I_3 = 34$ mA, $V_1 = 50$ V, $V_2 = 70$ V, $V_3 = 170$ V

11. $R_{3,4} = 2\ \Omega$. At junction of R_1, R_2,
and $R_{3,4}$: $I_1 + I_2 - I_{3,4} = 0$, $6I_1 + 2I_{3,4} = 12$
and $6I_2 = 2I_{3,4} = 6 \rightarrow I_1 = 1.4$ A, $I_2 = 400$ mA,
$I_3 = I_4 = 900$ mA

12. $I_1 = I_2 = I_3 = I_4 = 400$ mA

CHAPTER 16   Network Theorems

Exercise 16.1   Superposition Theorem

1. Short out 6-V source: $I = \dfrac{9}{78} = 115$ mA; Short out 9-V source: $I = \dfrac{6}{78} = 77$ mA $\rightarrow$

    $I_T = 115 + 77 \approx 190$ mA, $V_1 = (0.19)(24) = 4.6$ V, $V_2 = 3.5$ V, $V_3 = 6.9$ V

2. Short out 32-V source: $I_1 = \dfrac{24}{75} = 320$ mA, $I_2 = \dfrac{24}{255} = 107$ mA

    Short out 24-V source: $I_1 = \dfrac{32}{75} = 427$ mA, $I_2 = \dfrac{32}{255} = 142$ mA $\rightarrow$

    Resultant $I_1 = 427 - 320 \approx 110$ mA, $I_2 = 142 - 107 = 35$ mA

    $V_1 = 8.0$ V, $V_2 = 2.7$ V, $V_3 = 5.3$ V

3. Short out 20-V source: $I_1 = 0$, $I_2 = \dfrac{24}{300} = 80$ mA

    Short out 24-V source: $I_1 = \dfrac{20}{200} = 100$ mA, $I_2 = \dfrac{20}{300} = 66.7$ mA $\rightarrow$

    Resultant $I_1 = 100 + 0 = 100$ mA, $I_2 = 80 - 66.7 = 13$ mA,

    $V_1 = 20$ V, $V_2 = 4.0$ V

4. Short out 20-V source: $I_1 = 0$, $I_2 = \dfrac{24}{50} = 480$ mA

    Short out 24-V source: $I_1 = \dfrac{20}{100} = 200$ mA, $I_2 = \dfrac{20}{50} = 40$ mA $\rightarrow$

    Resultant $I_1 = 200 + 0 = 200$ mA, $I_2 = 480 - 400 = 80$ mA,

    $V_1 = 20$ V, $V_2 = 4.0$ V

5. Short out 12-V source: $R_T = 20 + \dfrac{50}{15} = 23.3$ Ω, $I_2 = \dfrac{18}{23.3} = 771$ mA,

    $I_1 = \dfrac{5}{15}(771) = 257$ mA, $I_3 = \left(\dfrac{10}{15}\right)(771) = 514$ mA; Short out 18-V source:

    $R_T = 10 + \dfrac{100}{25} = 14$ Ω, $I_1 = \dfrac{12}{14} = 857$ mA, $I_2 = \left(\dfrac{5}{15}\right)(857) = 171$ mA,

    $I_3 = \dfrac{20}{25}(857) = 686$ mA $\rightarrow$ Resultant $I_1 = 857 - 257 = 600$ mA, $I_2 = 771 - 171 = 600$ mA,

    $I_3 = 514 + 686 = 1.2$ A, $V_1 = 6.0$ V, $V_2 = 12$ V, $V_3 = 6.0$ V

6. Short out 15-V source: $R_T = 20 + \dfrac{100}{20} = 25$ Ω, $I_2 = \dfrac{30}{25} = 1.2$ A, $I_1 = \dfrac{10}{20}(1.2) = 600$ mA,

    $I_3 = \left(\dfrac{10}{20}\right)(1.2) = 600$ mA; Short out 30-V source: $R_T = 10 + \dfrac{200}{30} = 16.7$ Ω, $I_1 = \dfrac{15}{16.7} = 898$ mA,

    $I_2 = \left(\dfrac{10}{30}\right)(898) = 299$ mA, $I_3 = \dfrac{20}{30}(898) = 599$ mA $\rightarrow$ Resultant $I_1 = 898 - 600 \approx 300$ mA,

    $I_2 = 1200 - 299 \approx 900$ mA, $I_3 = 600 + 599 = 1.2$ A, $V_1 = 3.0$ V, $V_2 = 18$ V, $V_3 = 12$ V

7. Short out 12-V source: $R_T = 2.0 + \left(\dfrac{6.0}{5.0}\right) = 3.2$ kΩ, $I_1 = \dfrac{10}{3.2} = 3.125$ mA, $I_2 = \left(\dfrac{2}{5}\right)(3.125) = 1.25$ mA,

$I_3 = \left(\dfrac{3}{5}\right)(3.125) = 1.875$ mA; Short out 10-V source: $R_T = 3.0 + \left(\dfrac{4.0}{4.0}\right) = 4.0$ kΩ, $I_2 = \dfrac{12}{4} = 3.0$ mA,

$I_1 = \left(\dfrac{2}{4}\right)(3.0) = 1.5$ mA, $I_3 = \dfrac{2}{4}(3.0) = 1.5$ mA $\rightarrow$ Resultant $I_1 = 3.125 + 1.5 \approx 4.6$ mA,

$I_2 = 1.25 + 3.0 \approx 4.3$ mA, $I_3 = 1.875 - 1.5 = 0.38$ mA $= 380$ μA, $V_1 = 9.3$ V, $V_2 = 13$ V, $V_3 = 750$ mV

8. 540 mA, 460 mA, 86 mA, 8.1 V, 6.9 V, 860 mV

Exercise 16.2 Thevenin's Theorem

1. Remove R_L: $V_{TH} = \left(\dfrac{6}{11}\right)(9) = 4.91$ V, $R_{TH} = 3 + \left(\dfrac{6 \cdot 5}{11}\right) = 5.72$ Ω $\rightarrow$ $I_L = \dfrac{4.91}{14.72} = 0.334 \approx 330$ mA,

$V_L = (0.334)(9) = 3.0$ V

2. Remove R_L: $V_{TH} = \left(\dfrac{2}{4}\right)(60) = 30$ V, $R_{TH} = 1000 + \dfrac{2000}{2} = 2$ kΩ $\rightarrow$ $I_L = \dfrac{30}{3000} = 10$ mA,

$V_L = (0.010)(1000) = 10$ V

3. (a) Remove R_L: $V_{TH} = \left(\dfrac{2000}{3000}\right)(120) = 80$ V, $R_{TH} = \left(\dfrac{1000 \cdot 2000}{3000}\right) = 667 \approx 670$ Ω $\rightarrow$

$I_L = \dfrac{80}{3667} = 0.0218 \approx 22$ mA, $V_L = (0.0218)(3000) = 65$ V

(b) $R_T = 1000 + \left(\dfrac{3000 \cdot 2000}{5000}\right) = 2200$ Ω, $I_T = \dfrac{120}{2200} = 545$ mA $\rightarrow$ $I_L = \left(\dfrac{2000}{5000}\right)(545) = 0.0218 \approx 22$ mA,

$V_L = (0.0218)(3000) = 65$ V

4. (a) Remove R_L: $V_{TH} = \left(\dfrac{100}{200}\right)(36) = 18$ V, $R_{TH} = \left(\dfrac{100}{2}\right) = 50$ Ω $\rightarrow$ $I_L = \dfrac{18}{100} = 180$ mA,

$V_L = (0.180)(50) = 9.0$ V

(b) $R_T = 100 + \left(\dfrac{50 \cdot 100}{150}\right) = 133$ Ω, $I_T = \dfrac{36}{133} = 270$ mA $\rightarrow$ $I_L = \left(\dfrac{100}{150}\right)(270) = 180$ mA,

$V_L = (0.180)(50) = 9.0$ V

5. Remove R_L: $V_T = 15 - 12 = 3$ V $\rightarrow$ $V_2 = \left(\dfrac{5}{9}\right)(3) = 1.67$ V $\rightarrow$ $V_{TH} = 15 - 1.67 = 13.33 \approx 13$ V,

$R_{TH} = \left(\dfrac{4 \cdot 5}{9}\right) = 2.22 \approx 2.2$ Ω, $I_L = \dfrac{13.33}{8.22} = 1.62 \approx 1.6$ A, $V_L = (1.62)(6) = 9.7$ V

6. Remove R_L: $V_T = 80 - 65 = 15$ V $\rightarrow$ $V_2 = \left(\dfrac{200}{300}\right)(15) = 10$ V; $V_{TH} = 65 + 10 = 75$ V,

$R_{TH} = \left(\dfrac{100 \cdot 200}{300}\right) = 66.66 \approx 67$ Ω, $I_L = \dfrac{75}{166.7} = 450$ mA, $V_L = (0.450)(100) = 45$ V

7. Remove R_L: $V_2 = \left(\dfrac{2000}{5000}\right)(22) = 8.8$ V $\rightarrow$ $V_{TH} = 24 + 8.8 = 32.8 \approx 33$ V,

$R_{TH} = \left(\dfrac{2000 \cdot 3000}{5000}\right) = 1.2$ kΩ, $I_L = \dfrac{32.8}{2700} = 12$ mA, $V_L = (0.012)(1500) = 18$ V

8. Remove R_L: $V_2 = \left(\dfrac{100}{300}\right)(12) = 4.0$ V $\rightarrow$ $V_{TH} = 9 + 4.0 = 13$ V, $R_{TH} = \left(\dfrac{200 \cdot 100}{300}\right) = 66.7 \approx 67$ Ω,

$I_L = \dfrac{13}{117} = 110$ mA, $V_L = (0.11)(50) = 5.6$ V

9. (a) Remove R_L: $V_T = 8.0 - 6.0 = 2.0$ V $\rightarrow$ $V_1 = \left(\dfrac{20}{50}\right)(2.0) = 0.80$ V $\rightarrow$ $V_{TH} = 6.0 + 0.8 = 6.8$ V,

$R_{TH} = \left(\dfrac{20 \cdot 30}{50}\right) = 12$ Ω $\rightarrow$ $I_L = \dfrac{6.8}{37} = 0.184 \approx 180$ mA, $V_L = (0.184)(25) = 4.6$ V

(b) Short out 8-V source: $R_T = 20 + \left(\dfrac{25 \cdot 30}{55}\right) = 33.6$ Ω, $I_T = \dfrac{6.0}{33.6} = 0.178$ A $\rightarrow$

$I_L = \left(\dfrac{30}{55}\right)(0.178) = 0.0973$ A

Short out 6-V source: $R_T = 30 + \left(\dfrac{25 \cdot 20}{45}\right) = 41.1$ Ω, $I_T = \dfrac{8.0}{41.1} = 0.195$ A $\rightarrow$

$I_L = \left(\dfrac{20}{45}\right)(0.195) = 0.0867$ A

Resultant $I_L = 0.0973 + 0.0867 \approx 180$ mA, $V_L = 4.6$ V

10. (a) Remove R_L: $V_T = 28 - 20 = 8.0$ V $\rightarrow$ $V_1 = \left(\dfrac{60}{100}\right)(8.0) = 4.8$ V $\rightarrow$ $V_{TH} = 28 - 4.8 = 23.2 \approx 23$ V,

$R_{TH} = \left(\dfrac{60 \cdot 40}{100}\right) = 24$ Ω $\rightarrow$ $I_L = \dfrac{23.2}{124} = 0.187 \approx 190$ mA, $V_L = (0.187)(100) = 19$ V

(b) Short out 20-V source: $R_T = 60 + \left(\dfrac{100 \cdot 40}{140}\right) = 88.6$ Ω, $I_T = \dfrac{28}{88.6} = 0.316$ A $\rightarrow$

$I_L = \left(\dfrac{40}{140}\right)(0.316) = 0.0903$ A

Short out 28-V source: $R_T = 40 + \left(\dfrac{100 \cdot 60}{160}\right) = 77.5$ Ω, $I_T = \dfrac{20}{77.5} = 0.258$ A $\rightarrow$

$I_L = \left(\dfrac{60}{160}\right)(0.258) = 0.0968$ A

Resultant $I_L = 0.0903 + 0.0968 \approx 190$ mA, $V_L = 19$ V

Exercise 16.3 Norton's Theorem

1. (a) Remove R_3 and short terminals: $I_N = \dfrac{14}{6} = 2.33 \approx 2.3$ A;

   Short voltage source: $R_N = \left(\dfrac{6 \cdot 8}{14}\right) = 3.43 \approx 3.4$ Ω, $R_{N,L} = \dfrac{10(3.43)}{13.43} = 2.55$ Ω, $V_L = 2.33(2.55) \approx 6.0$ V,

   $I_L = \dfrac{6.0}{10} = 600$ mA

   (b) $R_T = 6 + \left(\dfrac{8 \cdot 10}{18}\right) = 10.4$ Ω, $I_T = \dfrac{14}{10.4} = 1.34$ A $\rightarrow I_3 = \left(\dfrac{8}{18}\right)(1.34) = 600$ mA, $V_3 = 6.0$ V

2. (a) Remove R_1 and short terminals: $R_T = \left(\dfrac{100 \cdot 300}{400}\right) = 75$ Ω, $I_N = \dfrac{24}{75} = 320$ mA;

   Short voltage source: $R_N = \left(\dfrac{100 \cdot 300}{400}\right) = 75$ Ω, $R_{N,L} = \dfrac{50(75)}{125} = 30$ Ω $\rightarrow V_L = 0.32(30) = 9.6$ V,

   $I_L = \dfrac{9.6}{50} \approx 190$ mA

   (b) $R_T = 50 + \left(\dfrac{100 \cdot 300}{400}\right) = 125$ Ω, $I_1 = \dfrac{24}{125} = 190$ mA, $V_1 = 9.6$ V

3. (a) Remove R_L and short terminals: $R_T = 200 + \left(\dfrac{100}{2}\right) = 250$ Ω, $I_T = \dfrac{50}{250} = 200$ mA $\rightarrow I_N = \dfrac{200}{2} = 100$ mA;

   Short voltage source: $R_N = 100 + \left(\dfrac{100 \cdot 200}{300}\right) = 166.7 \approx 170$ Ω, $R_{N,L} = \dfrac{300(167)}{467} = 107$ Ω $\rightarrow$

   $V_L = 0.1(107) = 10.7 \approx 11$ V, $I_L = \dfrac{10.7}{300} \approx 36$ mA

   (b) Remove R_L: $V_{TH} = \left(\dfrac{100}{300}\right)(50) = 16.7$ V, $R_{TH} = 100 + \left(\dfrac{100 \cdot 200}{300}\right) = 166.7 \approx 170$ Ω, $I_L = \dfrac{16.7}{466.7} = 36$ mA,

   $V_L = 11$ V

4. (a) Remove R_L and short terminals: $R_T = 5 + \left(\dfrac{7 \cdot 3}{10}\right) = 7.1$ Ω, $I_T = \dfrac{12}{7.1} = 1.69$ A $\rightarrow$

   $I_N = (1.69)\left(\dfrac{7}{10}\right) = 1.18 \approx 1.2$ A;

   Short voltage source: $R_N = 3 + \left(\dfrac{5 \cdot 7}{12}\right) = 5.92 \approx 5.9$ Ω, $R_{N,L} = \dfrac{5(5.9)}{10.9} = 2.71$ Ω $\rightarrow$

   $V_L = 1.18(2.71) = 3.2$ V, $I_L = \dfrac{3.2}{5} = 640$ mA

   (b) Remove R_L: $V_{TH} = \left(\dfrac{7}{12}\right)(12) = 7.0$ V, $R_{TH} = 3 + \left(\dfrac{5 \cdot 7}{12}\right) = 5.92 \approx 5.9$ Ω $\rightarrow I_L = \dfrac{7.0}{10.9} = 640$ mA, $V_L = 3.2$ V

5. Thevinin: $I_L = \dfrac{10}{25} = 400$ mA, $V_L = (0.4)(5) = 2.0$ V

   Norton: $I_L = (0.5)\left(\dfrac{20}{25}\right) = 400$ mA, $V_L = 2.0$ V

6. Thevinin: $I_L = \dfrac{150}{1100} = 140$ mA, $V_L = (0.14)(1000) = 140$ V

   Norton: $I_L = (1.5)\left(\dfrac{100}{1100}\right) = 140$ mA, $V_L = 140$ V

Review Exercises

1. (a) Short out 6-V source: $I = \dfrac{9}{18} = 500$ mA;

Short out 9-V source: $I = \dfrac{6}{18} = 333$ mA $\rightarrow I_T = 830$ mA, $V_1 = (.83)(10) = 8.3$ V,

$V_2 = 4.2$ V, $V_3 = 2.5$ V

(b) $V_T = 9 + 6 = 15$ V, $I_T = \dfrac{15}{18} = 830$ mA

2. Short out 30-V source: $I_{1,3} = \dfrac{40}{4000} = 10$ mA, $I_2 = 0$ A;

Short out 40-V source: $R_T = 800\ \Omega$, $I_T = \dfrac{30}{800} = 37.5$ mA, $I_2 = \dfrac{30}{1000} = 30$ mA,

$I_{1,3} = 37.5 - 30 = 7.5$ mA $\rightarrow$

Resultant $I_1 = I_3 = 10 - 7.5 = 2.5$ mA, $I_2 = 30$ mA, $V_1 = 5$ V, $V_2 = 30$ V, $V_3 = 5$ V

3. Short out 50-V source: $R_T = 100 + \left(\dfrac{70 \cdot 50}{120}\right) = 129\ \Omega$, $I_2 = \dfrac{60}{129} = 465$ mA,

$I_1 = \left(\dfrac{70}{120}\right)(465) = 271$ mA, $I_3 = \left(\dfrac{50}{120}\right)(465) = 194$ mA;

Short out 60-V source: $R_T = 50 + \left(\dfrac{70 \cdot 100}{170}\right) = 91.2\ \Omega$, $I_1 = \dfrac{50}{91.2} = 548$ mA,

$I_2 = \left(\dfrac{70}{170}\right)(548) = 226$ mA, $I_3 = \left(\dfrac{100}{170}\right)(548) = 323$ mA $\rightarrow$

Resultant $I_1 = 548 - 271 \approx 280$ mA, $I_2 = 465 - 226 \approx 240$ mA, $I_3 = 194 + 323 \approx 520$ mA,

$V_1 = 14$ V, $V_2 = 24$ V, $V_3 = 36$ V

4. Short out 220-V source: $R_T = 3 + \dfrac{5(4)}{9} = 5.22$ kΩ, $I_2 = \dfrac{240}{5222} = 46$ mA,

$V_2 = 0.046(3000) = 138$ V, $V_{1,3} = 240 - 138 = 102$ V, $I_1 = \dfrac{102}{4000} = 25.5$ mA, $I_3 = 20.4$ mA;

Short out 240-V source: $R_T = 4 + \dfrac{5(3)}{8} = 5.88$ kΩ, $I_1 = \dfrac{220}{5880} = 37.4$ mA, $V_1 = 0.0375(4000) = 150$ V,

$V_{2,3} = 70$ V, $I_2 = \dfrac{70}{3000} = 23.3$ mA, $I_3 = 14$ mA $\rightarrow$ Resultant $I_1 = 12$ mA, $I_2 = 23$ mA, $I_3 = 34$ mA,

$V_1 = 48$ V, $V_2 = 68$ V, $V_3 = 170$ V

5. Remove R_3: $V_{TH} = 40 - 30 = 10$ V, $R_{TH} = 2.0$ k$\Omega \rightarrow I_L = I_3 = \dfrac{10}{4000} = 2.5$ mA,

$V_L = V_3 = (0.0025)(2000) = 5$ V

6. Remove R_3: $V_T = 60 - 50 = 10$ V, $I_T = \dfrac{10}{150} = 66.6$ mA, $V_1 = (0.0666)(50) = 3.33$ V $\rightarrow V_{TH} = 50 + 3.33 = 53.3 \approx 50$ V,

$$R_{TH} = \left(\frac{50 \cdot 100}{150}\right) \approx 33 \ \Omega \rightarrow I_L = I_3 = \frac{53.3}{103} = 520 \text{ mA}, \ V_L = V_3 = (0.52)(70) = 36 \text{ V}$$

7. (a) Remove R_L: $V_{TH} = \left(\dfrac{100}{180}\right)(100) = 56.6 \approx 56$ V, $R_{TH} = 60 + \left(\dfrac{80 \cdot 100}{180}\right) = 104 \approx 100 \ \Omega \rightarrow$

$$I_L = \frac{55.6}{164} = 0.339 \approx 340 \text{ mA}, \ V_L = (0.339)(60) = 20 \text{ V}$$

(b) $R_T = 80 + \dfrac{100(120)}{220} = 134.5 \approx 130 \ \Omega$, $I_1 = \dfrac{100}{134.5} = 740$ mA, $V_1 = 59$ V, $V_L = \dfrac{41}{2} = 20.5 \approx 20$ V,

$$I_L = \frac{20.5}{60} = 340 \text{ mA}$$

8. Remove R_3: $V_T = 240 - 220 = 20$ V $\rightarrow V_1 = \left(\dfrac{4000}{7000}\right)(20) = 11.4$ V, $V_{TH} = 220 + 11.4 \approx 230$ V,

$$R_{TH} = \left(\frac{4000 \cdot 3000}{7000}\right) \approx 1.7 \text{ k}\Omega \rightarrow I_L = I_3 = \frac{230}{6700} = 34 \text{ mA}, \ I_L = I_3 = (0.034)(5000) = 170 \text{ V}$$

9. (a) Short R_3: $I_N = \dfrac{100}{1200} = 83$ mA, $R_N = \dfrac{1200(3300)}{4500} = 880 \ \Omega$, $R_{N,L} = \dfrac{1500(880)}{2380} = 555 \ \Omega \rightarrow$

$$V_3 = 0.083(555) = 46 \text{ V}, \ I_3 = \frac{46}{1500} = 31 \text{ mA}$$

(b) $R_T = 1.2 + \dfrac{3.3(1.5)}{4.8} = 2.23$ kΩ, $I_1 = \dfrac{100}{2230} = 44.8$ mA, $V_1 = (0.0448)(1200) = 54$ V $\rightarrow V_3 = 100 - 54 = 46$ V,

$$I_3 = \frac{46}{1500} = 31 \text{ mA}$$

10. (a) Short R_L: $R_T = 10 + \dfrac{5}{2} = 12.5 \ \Omega$, $I_T = \dfrac{20}{12.5} = 1.6$ A $\rightarrow I_N = \dfrac{(1.6)}{2} = 0.8$ A $= 800$ mA,

$$R_N = 5 + \frac{10(5)}{15} = 8.33 \ \Omega, \ R_{N,L} = \frac{10(8.33)}{18.33} = 4.54 \ \Omega \rightarrow V_L = 0.8(4.54) = 3.6 \text{ V}, \ I_L = \frac{3.6}{10} = 360 \text{ mA}$$

(b) Remove R_L: $V_{TH} = \left(\dfrac{5}{15}\right)(20) = 6.66$ V, $R_{TH} = 5 + \dfrac{10(5)}{15} = 8.33 \ \Omega$, $I_L = \dfrac{6.66}{18.33} \approx 360$ mA,

$$V_L = 0.36(10) = 3.6 \text{ V}$$

11. Remove R_3: $V_2 = 30$ V $\rightarrow V_1 = 10$ V, $I_1 = I_N = \dfrac{10}{2000} = 5.0$ mA, $R_N = 2.0$ kΩ, $I_L = I_3 = \dfrac{5}{2} = 2.5$ mA,

$V_3 = 0.0025(2000) = 5$ V

12. Short R_L: $R_T = 80 + \left(\dfrac{60 \cdot 100}{160}\right) = 117.5 \ \Omega$, $I_T = \dfrac{100}{117.5} = 0.851$ A, $V_1 = 0.851(80) = 68$ V, $V_3 = 100 - 68 = 32$ V $\rightarrow$

$I_3 = I_N = \dfrac{32}{60} \approx 530$ mA, $R_N = 60 + \left(\dfrac{80 \cdot 100}{180}\right) = 104 \approx 100 \ \Omega$, $R_{N,L} = 38 \ \Omega \rightarrow V_L = (0.530)(38) = 20.2 \approx 20$ V,

$I_L = \dfrac{20.2}{60} \approx 340$ mA

CHAPTER 17 Trigonometry of the Right Triangle

Exercise 17.1 Angles and Triangles

1. 30°

2. 90°

3. 270°

4. 45°

5. 135°

6. 240°

7. 18°

8. 72°

9. 29°

10. 43°

11. 86°

12. 120°

13. 5.2°

14. 1.5°

15. $\dfrac{\pi}{3}$

16. $\dfrac{\pi}{4}$

17. 2π

18. π

19. $\dfrac{2\pi}{3}$

20. $\dfrac{5\pi}{6}$

21. $\dfrac{\pi}{18}$

22. $\dfrac{\pi}{9}$

23. 0.96 rad

24. 0.47 rad

25. 1.7 rad

26. 2.3 rad

27. 0.14 rad

28. 0.30 rad

29. 3.0 rad

30. 1.9 rad

31. $A = B = 70°$, $C = 110°$

32. $A = C = 125°$, $B = 55°$

33. $A = 60°$, $B = 30°$

34. $A = 49.7°$, $B = 40.3°$, $C = 139.7°$

35. $A = 50°$, $B = 100°$, $C = 30°$

36. $A = 60°$, $B = 85°$

37. $A = 35°$, $B = 55°$

38. $A = 40°$, $B = 50°$

39. $A = 0.97$ rad, $B = 2.2$ rad

40. $A = 0.84$ rad, $B = 2.4$ rad

41. $\dfrac{360}{12} = 30° = \dfrac{\pi}{6}$

42. $\dfrac{360}{24} = 15° = \dfrac{\pi}{12}$

43. (a) 36°

    (b) 1.2 rad

44. $120(180) = 22{,}000°/s$

Exercise 17.2 Pythagorean Theorem

1. 13

2. 17

3. 22

4. 7.6

5. 3.2

6. 290

7. 5.2

8. 3.8

9. 0.85

10. 600

11. $x = 3.6$, $y = 4.8$

12. $x = 7.5$, $y = 20$

13. $x = 3.5$, $y = 3$

14. $x = 3.0$, $y = 4.2$

15. $x = 1.4$, $y = 0.69$

16. $x = 5.4$, $y = 7.7$

17. $\dfrac{x}{6} = \dfrac{6}{8} \rightarrow x = 4.5$, $y = 7.5$

18. $x = 8.3$, $y = 6.7$

19. 6.4 ft

20. $40^2 + 35^2 = d^2 \rightarrow d = 53$ mi

21. $9^2 + 12^2 = d^2 \rightarrow d = 15$ mi

22. No, diagonal = 3.2 m

23. $\dfrac{h}{50} = \dfrac{36}{20} \rightarrow h = 90$ ft

24. $\dfrac{1.8}{1.5} = \dfrac{h}{11.8} \rightarrow h = 14$ m

25. 6.4 kΩ

26. 1.4 kΩ

27. 29 kΩ

28. 59 kΩ

29. 16 V

30. 140 V

31. $\dfrac{l}{27} = \dfrac{125}{20} \rightarrow l = 170$ mm

32. $\dfrac{25}{35} = 0.71$ mm

Exercise 17.3 Trigonometric Ratios

1. $\sin A = \cos B = 0.471$
   $\cos A = \sin B = 0.882$
   $\tan A = 0.533$, $\tan B = 1.88$

2. $\sin A = \cos B = 0.600$
   $\cos A = \sin B = 0.800$
   $\tan A = 0.750$, $\tan B = 1.33$

3. $\sin A = \cos B = 0.800$
   $\cos A = \sin B = 0.600$
   $\tan A = 1.33$, $\tan B = 0.750$

4. $\sin A = \cos B = 0.385$
$\cos A = \sin B = 0.923$
$\tan A = 0.417, \tan B = 2.40$

5. $\sin A = \cos B = 0.581$
$\cos A = \sin B = 0.814$
$\tan A = 0.714, \tan B = 1.4$

6. $\sin A = \cos B = 0.944$
$\sin B = \cos A = 0.333$
$\tan A = 2.83, \tan B = 0.353$

7. $\sin A = \cos B = 0.640$
$\cos A = \sin B = 0.768$
$\tan A = 0.833, \tan B = 1.2$

8. $\sin A = \cos B = 0.584$
$\sin B = \cos A = 0.812$
$\tan A = 0.719, \tan B = 1.39$

9. $\sin A = \cos B = 0.836$
$\cos A = \sin B = 0.549$
$\tan A = 1.52, \tan B = 0.656$

10. $\sin A = \cos B = 0.600$
$\cos A = \sin B = 0.800$
$\tan A = 0.750, \tan B = 1.33$

11. $\sin A = \cos B = 0.333$
$\cos A = \sin B = 0.943$
$\tan A = 0.354, \tan B = 2.83$

12. $\sin A = \cos B = 0.541$
$\sin B = \cos A = 0.841$
$\tan A = 0.643, \tan B = 1.55$

13. $\sin A = \cos B = 0.707$
$\cos A = \sin B = 0.707$
$\tan A = 1.00, \tan B = 1.00$

14. $\sin A = \cos B = 0.707$
$\sin B = \cos A = 0.707$
$\tan A = 1.00, \tan B = 1.00$

15. $\sin A = \cos B = 0.816$
$\cos A = \sin B = 0.577$
$\tan A = 1.41, \tan B = 0.707$

16. $\sin A = \cos B = 0.866$
$\sin B = \cos A = 0.500$
$\tan A = 1.73, \tan B = 0.577$

17. $\sin A = \cos B = 0.500$
$\cos A = \sin B = 0.866$
$\tan A = 0.577, \tan B = 1.73$

18. $\sin A = \cos B = 0.600$
$\sin B = \cos A = 0.800$
$\tan A = 0.750, \tan B = 1.33$

19. 0.500

20. 0.707

21. 0.176

22. 1.73

23. 0.163

24. 0.633

25. 1.96

26. 3.60

27. 0.853

28. 0.208

29. 0.866

30. 0.866

31. 1.00

32. 0.325

33. 60.0°

34. 66.4°

35. 19.3°

36. 40.5°

37. 45.0°

38. 60.0°

39. 65.0°

40. 30.0°

41. 22.6°

42. 5.65°

43. 60.0°

44. 45.0°

45. $B = 40.0°, a = 2.30, b = 1.93$

46. $A = 73.0°, a = 7.84, b = 2.40$

47. $A = 64.5°, b = 4.91, c = 11.4$

48. $B = 36.8°, b = 0.337, c = 0.562$

49. $A = 38.7°, B = 51.3°, b = 6.24$

50. $A = 22.0°, B = 68.0°, c = 6.69$

51. $A = 0.841 \text{ rad}, b = 4.03, c = 6.04$

52. $B = 0.471 \text{ rad}, b = 1.68, c = 3.70$

53. $B = 45.0°, b = 2.00, c = 2.83$

54. $A = 36.9°, B = 53.1°, a = 6.00, b = 8.00$

55. $60(\tan 56°) = 89 \text{ m}$

56. $100(\tan 23°) = 42 \text{ ft}$

57. $\dfrac{150}{\tan 11°} = 770 \text{ ft}$

58. 12°

59. $Z = 4.5 \text{ k}\Omega, \theta = 35°$

60. $V_T = 100 \text{ V}, \theta = 37°$

61. $v = 212 \text{ V}$

62. $\dfrac{\pi}{6} = 0.52 \text{ rad}$

63. $56° = 0.98 \text{ rad}$

64. $56° = 0.98 \text{ rad}$

Review Exercises

1. 60.0°

2. 150.0°

3. 12.0°

4. 68.0°

5. 86.0°

6. 19.5°

7. $\dfrac{\pi}{6} = 0.524 \text{ rad}$

8. $\dfrac{3\pi}{4} = 2.36 \text{ rad}$

9. $\dfrac{\pi}{9} = 0.349 \text{ rad}$

10. $\pi = 3.14 \text{ rad}$

11. 0.803 rad

12. $\dfrac{7\pi}{9} = 2.44 \text{ rad}$

13. $A = C = 70.0°, B = 110°$

14. $A = B = 40.0°, C = 50.0°$

15. 2.50

16. 26.0

17. 62.4

18. 3.04

19. 18.4

20. 13.0

21. $x = 4.00, y = 7.21$

22. $x = 3.00, y = 4.61$

23. $\sin A = \cos B = 0.800$
    $\cos A = \sin B = 0.600$
    $\tan A = 1.33, \tan B = 0.750$

24. $\sin A = \cos B = 0.471$
    $\sin B = \cos A = 0.882$
    $\tan A = 0.533, \tan B = 1.88$

25. $\sin A = \cos B = 0.385$
    $\cos A = \sin B = 0.923$
    $\tan A = 0.417, \tan B = 2.40$

26. $\sin A = \cos B = 0.514$
    $\sin B = \cos A = 0.857$
    $\tan A = 0.600, \tan B = 1.67$

27. $\sin A = \cos B = 0.680$
    $\sin B = \cos A = 0.733$
    $\tan A = 0.927, \tan B = 1.08$

28. $\sin A = \cos B = 0.750$
    $\sin B = \cos A = 0.661$
    $\tan A = 1.13, \tan B = 0.882$

29. $\sin A = \cos B = 0.600$
    $\sin B = \cos A = 0.800$
    $\tan A = 0.750, \tan B = 1.33$

30. $\sin A = \cos B = 0.567$
    $\sin B = \cos A = 0.824$
    $\tan A = 0.689, \tan B = 1.45$

31. 0.866

32. 0.707

33. 1.52

34. 2.75

35. 0.718

36. 0.808

37. 0.839

38. 0.577

39. 11.5°

40. 69.5°

41. 30.0°

42. 80.0°

43. 58.0°

44. 44.3°

45. 60°, 2.89, 5.77

46. 65°, 18.9, 20.8

47. 62°, 0.610, 1.15

48. 34°, 18.5, 27.4

49. 33.7°, 56.3°, 18.0

50. 0.921 rad, 9.87, 12.4

51. 36 mi

52. 167 ft

53. 75 m

54. $\sin^{-1}\left(\dfrac{200}{500}\right) = 24°$

55. (a) 8.5kΩ
    (b) 16°

56. (a) 730 Ω
    (b) 42°

57. $\dfrac{3}{10}$ as large: 3.6 mm × 7.2 mm

58. 65°, 25°

59. (a) 0.029°
    (b) 0.14°

60. (a) 87 rad/s
    (b) 100 rad/s
    (c) 100 rad/s

CHAPTER 18   Trigonometry of the Circle

Exercise 18.1   Trigonometric Functions

	[Sin,	Cos,	Tan]
1.	0.800,	0.600,	1.33
2.	0.600,	0.800,	0.750
3.	0.882,	−0.471,	−1.88
4.	0.923,	−0.385,	−2.40
5.	−0.385,	−0.923,	0.417
6.	−0.800,	−0.600,	1.33
7.	−0.600,	0.800,	−0.75
8.	−0.471,	0.882,	−0.533
9.	−0.707,	0.707,	−1.00
10.	−0.822,	0.569,	−1.44
11.	0.793,	0.609,	1.30
12.	0.800,	0.600,	1.33

	[Sin,	Cos,	Tan]
13.	0.809,	−0.588,	−1.38
14.	0.637,	−0.771,	−0.827
15.	−0.625,	−0.781,	0.800
16.	−0.610,	−0.793,	0.769
17.	−0.903,	0.430,	−2.10
18.	−0.524,	0.851,	−0.615

19. $\cos \theta = 0.800, \tan \theta = 0.750$

20. $\cos \theta = 0.385, \tan \theta = 2.40$

21. $\sin \theta = -0.923, \cos \theta = 0.385$

22. $\sin \theta = -0.600, \cos \theta = 0.800$

23. $\sin \theta = -0.943, \tan \theta = 2.83$

24. $\sin \theta = 0.866, \tan \theta = -1.73$

25. $\sin \theta = 0.832, \cos \theta = 0.555$

26. $\sin \theta = 0.949, \cos \theta = 0.316$

27. $\sin \theta = -0.714, \tan \theta = -1.02$

28. $\cos \theta = 0.917, \tan \theta = 0.436$

29. $\sin \theta = 0.707, \cos \theta = -0.707$

30. $\sin \theta = -0.800, \cos \theta = -0.600$

31. $\sin \theta = 0.422, \cos \theta = -0.906,$
    $\tan \theta = -0.467$

32. $\sin \theta = -0.755, \cos \theta = 0.656,$
    $\tan \theta = -1.15$

33. (a) $V_T = 18.4$ V
    (b) $\sin \theta = -0.652, \cos \theta = 0.759,$
    $\tan \theta = -0.857$

34. (a) $V_C = -28.6$
   (b) $\sin \theta = -0.715$, $\cos \theta = 0.700$, $\tan \theta = -1.02$

35. $\tan \phi z = 1.42$, $\tan \phi y = -1.42$

36. $\tan \phi z = 0.790$, $\tan \phi y = -0.790$

Exercise 18.2   Reference Angles and Special Angles

1. $\sin 50° = 0.766$

2. $\sin 60° = 0.866$

3. $-\tan 30° = -0.577$

4. $-\tan 70° = -2.75$

5. $\cos 15° = 0.966$

6. $\cos 60° = 0.500$

7. $-\tan 80° = -5.67$

8. $-\tan 45° = -1.00$

9. $-\sin 30° = -0.500$

10. $-\cos 45° = -0.707$

11. $-\tan 50.6° = -1.22$

12. $-\tan 48.2° = -1.12$

13. $\tan 63.0° = 1.97$

14. $\tan 66.4° = 2.29$

15. $\cos 90° = 0$

16. $\cos 180° = -1$

17. $\tan 180° = 0$

18. $\tan 0° = 0$

19. $\sin 270° = -1$

20. $\sin 60° = 0.866$

21. $-\tan 53° = -1.33$

22. $-\tan 6.7° = -0.117$

23. $-\sin 80° = -0.985$

24. $-\cos 30° = -0.866$

25. $\cos 0° = 1$

26. $\sin 270° = -1$

27. $-\tan 45° = -1.00$

28. $-\tan 30° = -0.578$

29. $-\tan 22.5° = -0.415$

30. $-\tan 15° = -0.268$

31. 9.00 knots

32. (a) 1020 m
   (b) 510 m

33. (a) -0.424
   (b) $X_C = 1.95$ kΩ, $Z = 5.00$ kΩ

34. (a) -1.48
   (b) $X_C = 3.15$ kΩ, $R = 2.12$ kΩ

35. (a) 850 mA
   (b) 736 mA
   (c) 0 mA
   (d) -601 mA

36. (a) 5.00 V
   (b) 10.0 V
   (c) -1.74 V
   (d) -9.36 V

37. (a) 114 V
   (b) -70.5 V
   (c) 0 V

38. (a) 34.2 V
   (b) -49.1 V
   (c) 0 V

Exercise 18.3   Inverse Functions

1. 30.0°

2. 30.0°

3. 50.0°

4. 67.9°

5. 72.7°

6. 12.7°

7. 142.0°

8. −5.7°

9. −41.9°

10. −28.5°

11. −60.0°

12. −45.0°

13. 25.0°, 335.0°

14. 39.0°, 141.0°

15. 40.2°, 220.2°

16. 51.2°, 231.2°

17. 213.8°, 326.2°

18. 97.6°, 262.4°

19. 153.3°, 333.3°

20. 116.5°, 296.5°

21. 99.0°, 279.0°

22. 176.8°, 356.8°

23. 0.981 rad, 5.30 rad

24. 3.82 rad, 5.60 rad

25. 2.36 rad, 5.50 rad

26. 0.983 rad, 4.12 rad

27. 3.67 rad, 5.76 rad

28. 0.841, 5.44 rad

29. 1.19 rad, 4.33 rad

30. 1.87 rad, 5.01 rad

31. $\sin \theta = \pm 0.707 \rightarrow \theta = 0.785$ rad, 2.36 rad, 3.93 rad, 5.50 rad

32. $\tan \theta = \pm 1.73 \rightarrow \theta = 1.05$ rad, 2.09 rad, 4.19 rad, 5.24 rad

33. −1.40, 125°

34. 8.24°

35. −1.50, −56.3°

36. −0.429, −23.2°

37. 333°, −27.0°

38. **(a) (b) & (c):** $\frac{\pi}{2}$ rad = 1.57 rad

(d) If $\tan \theta = x$, then:

$$\tan^{-1}\left(\frac{\pi}{2} - \theta\right) = \frac{1}{x}$$

and $\alpha = \theta + \left(\frac{\pi}{2} - \theta\right) = \frac{\pi}{2}$

39. **(a)** 0.629 rad, 2.51 rad

(b) 1.67 ms, 6.67 ms

40. **(a)** Ref. angle $= \cos^{-1}\left(\frac{1.5}{2.5}\right) \rightarrow \omega t = 0.927$ rad, 5.36 rad

(b) $t = \dfrac{0.927}{400} = 2.32$ ms and $\dfrac{5.36}{400} = 13.4$ ms

Review Exercises

	[*Sin*,	*Cos*,	*Tan*]
1.	0.923,	0.385,	2.40
2.	−0.600,	−0.800,	0.75
3.	0.882,	−0.471,	−1.88
4.	−0.280,	0.96,	−0.292
5.	−0.300,	0.954,	−0.314
6.	−0.894,	−0.447,	2.00

7. $-\sin 50° = -0.766$

8. $\cos 84° = 0.105$

9. $\tan 65° = 2.14$

10. $-\tan 56° = -1.48$

11. $-\tan 88.3° = -34.1$

12. $-\tan 44.1° = -0.970$

13. $77.5° = 1.35$ rad

14. $-30.4° = -0.530$ rad

15. $65.5° = 1.14$ rad

16. $28.8° = 0.503$ rad

17. $60° = 1.05$ rad, $300° = 5.24$ rad

18. $224° = 3.91$ rad, $316° = 5.51$ rad

19. $136° = 2.37$ rad, $316° = 5.51$ rad

20. $66.5° = 1.16$ rad, $247° = 4.30$ rad

21. $36.9° = 0.644$ rad, $143° = 2.50$ rad

22. $109° = 1.91$ rad, $251° = 4.37$ rad

23. $108° = 1.89$ rad, $288° = 5.03$ rad

24. $65.6° = 1.14$ rad, $246° = 4.29$ rad

25. 18.8 cm^2

26. **(a)** −0.625, 0.781, −0.800

(b) 19.2 mi/h, $-38.7° = -0.675$ rad

27. **(a)** −4.00 A

(b) −1.70 A

(c) −0.351 A = −351 mA

28. **(a)** Ref. angle $= \cos^{-1}\left(\frac{3}{4}\right) \rightarrow 2\pi f t = 0.723$ rad

at $t = \dfrac{0.723}{(120\pi)} = 1.92$ ms and $2\pi f t = 5.56$ rad

at $t = 14.7$ ms

(b) $2\pi f t = 2.09$ rad at $t = 5.56$ ms and 4.19 rad at $t = 11.1$ ms

29. 40.5 mA, −32.9°

30. 10.6 N/C, 302°, −57.6°

CHAPTER 19   Alternating Current

Exercise 19.1   Alternating Current Waves

1.

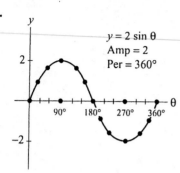

$y = 2 \sin \theta$
Amp = 2
Per = 360°

2.

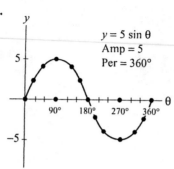

$y = 5 \sin \theta$
Amp = 5
Per = 360°

3.

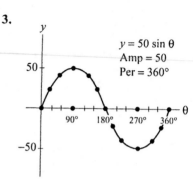

$y = 50 \sin \theta$
Amp = 50
Per = 360°

4.

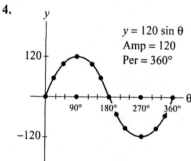

$y = 120 \sin \theta$
Amp = 120
Per = 360°

5.

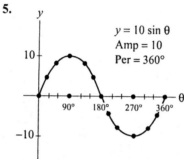

$y = 10 \sin \theta$
Amp = 10
Per = 360°

6.

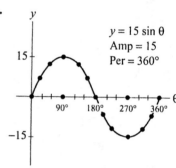

$y = 15 \sin \theta$
Amp = 15
Per = 360°

7.

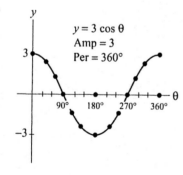

$y = 3 \cos \theta$
Amp = 3
Per = 360°

8.

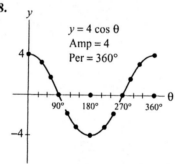

$y = 4 \cos \theta$
Amp = 4
Per = 360°

9.

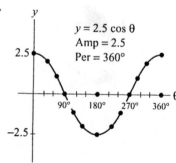

$y = 2.5 \cos \theta$
Amp = 2.5
Per = 360°

10.

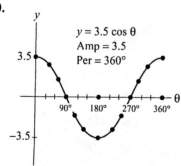

$y = 3.5 \cos \theta$
Amp = 3.5
Per = 360°

11.

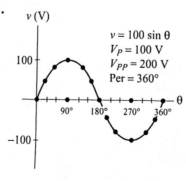

$v = 100 \sin \theta$
$V_P = 100$ V
$V_{PP} = 200$ V
Per = 360°

12.

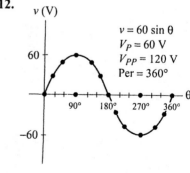

$v = 60 \sin \theta$
$V_P = 60$ V
$V_{PP} = 120$ V
Per = 360°

13.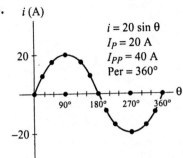

$i = 20 \sin \theta$
$I_P = 20$ A
$I_{PP} = 40$ A
Per = 360°

14.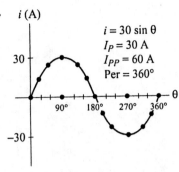

$i = 30 \sin \theta$
$I_P = 30$ A
$I_{PP} = 60$ A
Per = 360°

15.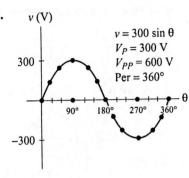

$v = 300 \sin \theta$
$V_P = 300$ V
$V_{PP} = 600$ V
Per = 360°

16.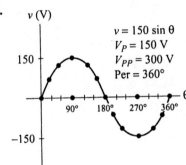

$v = 150 \sin \theta$
$V_P = 150$ V
$V_{PP} = 300$ V
Per = 360°

17.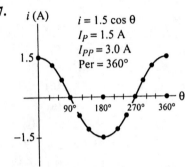

$i = 1.5 \cos \theta$
$I_P = 1.5$ A
$I_{PP} = 3.0$ A
Per = 360°

18.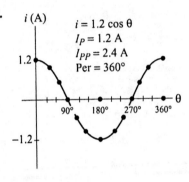

$i = 1.2 \cos \theta$
$I_P = 1.2$ A
$I_{PP} = 2.4$ A
Per = 360°

19.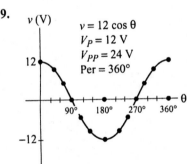

$v = 12 \cos \theta$
$V_P = 12$ V
$V_{PP} = 24$ V
Per = 360°

20.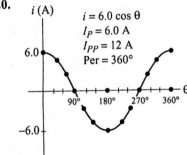

$i = 6.0 \cos \theta$
$I_P = 6.0$ A
$I_{PP} = 12$ A
Per = 360°

21.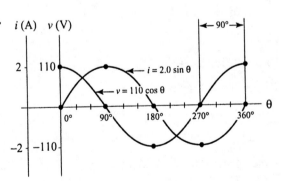

$i = 2.0 \sin \theta$
$v = 110 \cos \theta$

22.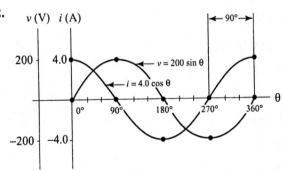

$v = 200 \sin \theta$
$i = 4.0 \cos \theta$

23. (a) 39 V

(b) Ref. angle = $\sin^{-1}\left(\dfrac{50}{100}\right) \rightarrow \omega t = 0.52$ rad, 2.6 rad

24. (a) 850 mA

(b) 0.34 rad, 2.8 rad

Exercise 19.2   Root Mean Square Values

1. 300 V, 210 V

2. 320 V, 110 V

3. 4.4 A, 1.6 A

4. 11 A, 4.0 A

5. 280 V, 99 V

6. 200 V, 71 V

7. 300 mA, 110 mA

8. 760 mA, 270 mA

9. 11 A, 4.0 A

10. 76 mA, 27 mA

11. 160 V, 320 V

12. 330 V, 660 V

13. 1.7 A, 3.4 A

14. 4.7 A, 9.4 A

15. 850 mA, 1.7 A

16. 35 mA, 70 mA

17. 110 V, 220 V

18. 51 V, 102 V

19. 110 mA, 220 mA

20. 170 mA, 340 mA

21. 110 V, 160 V, 2.2 A, 3.1 A, 240 W

22. 110 V, 160 V, 22 mA, 31 mA, 2.5 W

23. **(a)** 33 V, 11 V, 17 V, 5.5 V
    (b) 610 mW, 910 mW, 300 mW, 1.8 W

24. **(a)** 28 mA, 21 V, 34 V, 45 V
    (b) 600 mW, 950 mW, 1.3 W, 2.8 W

25. **(a)** 67 mA, 53 mA, 120 mA
    (b) 5.3 W, 4.3 W, 9.6 W

26. **(a)** 220 V, 430 mA, 780 mA
    (b) 76 W, 94 W, 170 W

Exercise 19.3   Frequency and Period

1. 55 Hz, 18 ms

2. 65 Hz, 15 ms

3. 70 Hz, 14 ms

4. 50 Hz, 20 ms

5. 60 Hz, 17 ms

6. 59 Hz, 17 ms

7. 48 Hz, 21 ms

8. 51 Hz, 20 ms

9. 840 kHz, 1.2 μs

10. 95 kHz, 10 μs

11. 12 kHz, 84 μs

12. 1.4 MHz, 710 ns

13. 17 ms, 120π rad/s

14. 20 ms, 100π rad/s

15. 22 ms, 90π rad/s

16. 13 ms, 150π rad/s

17. 2.0 ms, 1000π rad/s

18. 10 ms, 200π rad/s

19. 1.1 μs, 5.7×10^6 rad/s

20. 17 μs, 380×10^3 rad/s

21. 14 ns, 440×10^6 rad/s

22. 10 ns, 630×10^6 rad/s

23. 4.0 A, 120π rad/s, $\dfrac{120\pi}{2\pi} = 60$ Hz, $\dfrac{1}{60} = 17$ ms

24. 1.0 A, 100π rad/s, 50 Hz, 20 ms

25. 110 V, 140π rad/s, 70 Hz, 14 ms

26. 90 V, 150π rad/s, 75 Hz, 13 ms

27. 310 V, 300 rad/s, 48 Hz, 21 ms

28. 170 V, 400 rad/s, 64 Hz, 16 ms

29. 450 mA, 500 rad/s, 80 Hz, 13 ms

30. 650 mA, 800 rad/s, 130 Hz, 7.9 ms

31. 72 V, 3.0×10^6 rad/s, 480 kHz, 2.1 μs

32. 6.4 A, 200×10^6 rad/s, 32 MHz, 31 ns

33. Period = 16 ms, $f = \dfrac{1}{0.016} = 63$ Hz,
    $\omega = 2\pi(63) = 390$ rad/s

34. 350 rad/s, 56 Hz, 18 ms

35. $v = 180 \sin 120\pi t$

36. $v = 90 \sin 100\pi t$

37. $i = 2.5 \sin 100\pi t$

38. $i = 0.33 \sin 120\pi t$

39. $i = 0.45 \sin 420t$

40. $i = 4.0 \sin 310t$

41. $v = 160 \sin 290t$

42. $v = 130 \sin 350t$

43.

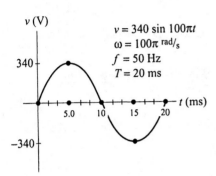

$v = 340 \sin 100\pi t$
$\omega = 100\pi \; ^{rad}/_s$
$f = 50$ Hz
$T = 20$ ms

44.

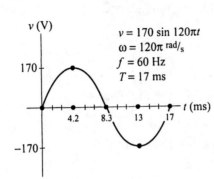

$v = 170 \sin 120\pi t$
$\omega = 120\pi \; ^{rad}/_s$
$f = 60$ Hz
$T = 17$ ms

45.

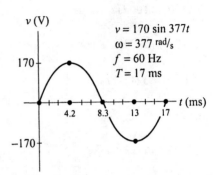

$v = 170 \sin 377t$
$\omega = 377 \; ^{rad}/_s$
$f = 60$ Hz
$T = 17$ ms

46.

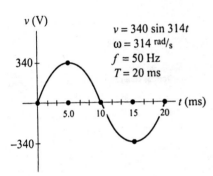

$v = 340 \sin 314t$
$\omega = 314 \; ^{rad}/_s$
$f = 50$ Hz
$T = 20$ ms

47.

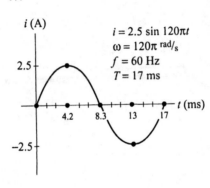

$i = 2.5 \sin 120\pi t$
$\omega = 120\pi \; ^{rad}/_s$
$f = 60$ Hz
$T = 17$ ms

48.

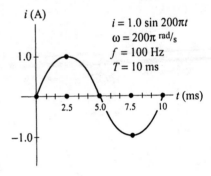

$i = 1.0 \sin 200\pi t$
$\omega = 200\pi \; ^{rad}/_s$
$f = 100$ Hz
$T = 10$ ms

49.

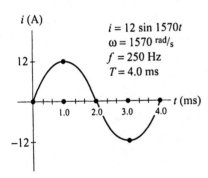

$i = 12 \sin 1570t$
$\omega = 1570 \; ^{rad}/_s$
$f = 250$ Hz
$T = 4.0$ ms

50.

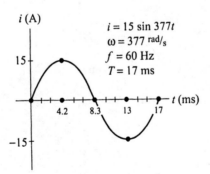

$i = 15 \sin 377t$
$\omega = 377 \; ^{rad}/_s$
$f = 60$ Hz
$T = 17$ ms

51. **(a)** $v = 160 \sin [120\pi(0.007)] = 77$ V and $v = 86$ V

(b) Ref. angle $= \sin^{-1}\left(\dfrac{100}{160}\right) \rightarrow 120\pi t = 0.675$ rad,

and 2.47 rad $\rightarrow t = \dfrac{0.675}{120\pi} = 1.8$ ms and

$t = 6.5$ ms

52. **(a)** -240 V, 300 V
  (b) 11 ms, 19 ms

53. **(a)** 1.2 A, 910 mA
  (b) 12 ms, 18 ms

54. **(a)** -1.8 A, 1.3 A
  (b) 1.9 ms, 6.4 ms

Exercise 19.4 Phase Angle

1. 1.5 A, 50 Hz, 20 ms, $\dfrac{\pi}{2}$

2. 2.3 A, 60 Hz, 17 ms, $\dfrac{\pi}{2}$

3. 300 V, 100 Hz, 10 ms, $\dfrac{\pi}{2}$

4. 170 V, 55 Hz, 18 ms, $-\dfrac{\pi}{2}$

5. 60 V, 60 Hz, 17 ms, $-\dfrac{\pi}{2}$

6. 80 V, 50 Hz, 20 ms, $\dfrac{\pi}{2}$

7. 18 A, 50 Hz, 20 ms, $\dfrac{\pi}{2}$

8. 16 A, 60 Hz, 17 ms, $\dfrac{\pi}{2}$

9. $i = 3.3 \sin\left(120\pi t + \dfrac{\pi}{2}\right)$

10. $i = 7.5 \sin 120\pi t$

11. $v = 400 \sin 100\pi t$

12. $v = 380 \sin\left(100\pi t + \dfrac{\pi}{2}\right)$

13. $v = 350 \sin\left(100\pi t + \dfrac{\pi}{2}\right)$

14. $v = 150 \sin\left(120\pi t - \dfrac{\pi}{2}\right)$

15. $i = 12 \sin 120\pi t$

16. $i = 10 \sin 100\pi t$

17. $v = 170 \sin\left(350t + \dfrac{\pi}{2}\right)$

18. $v = 160 \sin(390t + \pi)$

19. $i = 0.50 \sin\left(100\pi t - \dfrac{\pi}{2}\right)$

20. $i = 0.80 \sin\left(80\pi t + \dfrac{\pi}{2}\right)$

21. (a)

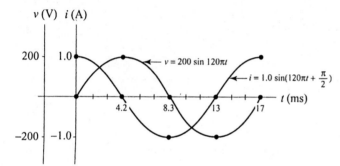

(b) t difference = 4.2 ms

22. (a)

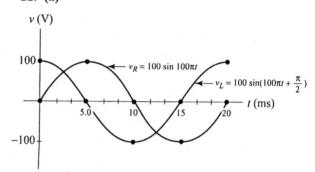

(b) t difference = 5.0 ms

23. (a) Both: Period = 20 ms,

$f = \dfrac{1}{20} = 50$ Hz;

v: $\phi = \dfrac{\pi}{2}$ rad, i: $\phi = 0$ rad

(b) 5 ms, v leads i by $\dfrac{\pi}{2}$

24. (a) Both: 16 ms, 63 Hz; v: 0 rad,

i: $\dfrac{\pi}{2}$ rad

(b) 4.0 ms, v lags i by $\dfrac{\pi}{2}$

25. (a) $i = 3.1 \sin\left(0.720\pi + \dfrac{\pi}{2}\right)$

$= -2.0$ A and $i = 1.7$ A

(b) $i = 0.0$ A $\rightarrow \sin^{-1}\left(120\pi\, t + \dfrac{\pi}{2}\right) = 0$

$0 \rightarrow 120\pi t + \dfrac{\pi}{2} = \pi$

and $2\pi \rightarrow t = \dfrac{1}{240} = 4.2$ ms

and $t = \dfrac{3}{240} = 13$ ms

26. (a) 0.0 V, 140 V

(b) 10 ms

Review Exercises

1.

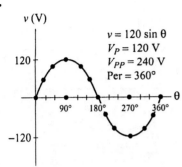

$v = 120 \sin \theta$
$V_P = 120$ V
$V_{PP} = 240$ V
Per = 360°

2.

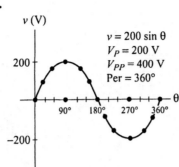

$v = 200 \sin \theta$
$V_P = 200$ V
$V_{PP} = 400$ V
Per = 360°

3.

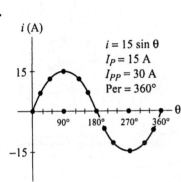

$i = 15 \sin \theta$
$I_P = 15$ A
$I_{PP} = 30$ A
Per = 360°

4.

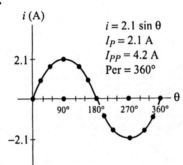

$i = 2.1 \sin \theta$
$I_P = 2.1$ A
$I_{PP} = 4.2$ A
Per = 360°

5. 160 V, 113 V, 120π rad/s, 60 Hz, 17 ms, 0 rad

6. 100 V, 71 V, 150π rad/s, 75 Hz, 13 ms, 0 rad

7. 3.0 A, 2.1 A, 200π rad/s, 100 Hz, 10 ms, 0 rad

8. 11 A, 7.8 A, 100π rad/s, 50 Hz, 20 ms, 0 rad

9. 170 V, 120 V, 350 rad/s, 56 Hz, 18 ms, 0 rad

10. 240 mA, 170 mA, 380 rad/s, 60 Hz, 17 ms, 0 rad

11. 1.2 A, 850 mA, 140π rad/s, 70 Hz, 14 ms, $\frac{\pi}{2}$ rad

12. 5.6 A, 4.0 A, 314 rad/s, 50 Hz, 20 ms, $\frac{\pi}{2}$ rad

13. 320 V, 230 V, 377 rad/s, 60 Hz, 17 ms, $\frac{\pi}{2}$ rad

14. 50 V, 35 V, 120π rad/s, 60 Hz, 17 ms, $-\frac{\pi}{2}$ rad

15. $i = 2.4 \sin 20\pi t$

16. $i = 5.5 \sin 120\pi t$

17. $v = 110 \sin 100\pi t$

18. $v = 50 \sin 100\pi t$

19. $v = 120 \sin 370t$

20. $i = 14 \sin 330t$

21. $i = 14 \sin\left(100\pi t + \frac{\pi}{2}\right)$

22. $v = 300 \sin\left(100\pi t + \frac{\pi}{2}\right)$

23. $v = 220 \sin\left(120\pi t + \frac{\pi}{2}\right)$

24. $i = 1.5 \sin\left(50\pi t - \frac{\pi}{2}\right)$

25. 50 mA, 71 mA, 75 V, 110 V, 3.8 W

26. **(a)** 10 A, 14 A, 170 V, 4.0 A, 6.0 A
  (b) 480 W, 720 W, 1200 W

27. **(a)** Period = 4(3 ms) = 12 ms, $f = \dfrac{1}{0.012} = 83$ Hz,
  $\omega = 2\pi(83) = 520$ rad/s

  (b) $v = 120 \sin 520t$

28. **(a)** Both: Period = 10 ms, $f = \dfrac{1}{0.010} = 100$ Hz,
  $\omega = 200\pi$ rad/s

  (b) $\dfrac{\pi}{2}$ rad, 2.5 ms

29.

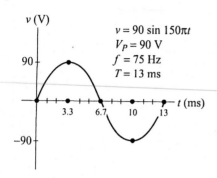

$v = 90 \sin 150\pi t$
$V_P = 90$ V
$f = 75$ Hz
$T = 13$ ms

30. (a) $v_R = 200 \cos 120\pi t$ or $v_R = 200 \sin\left(120\pi t + \dfrac{\pi}{2}\right)$

(b)

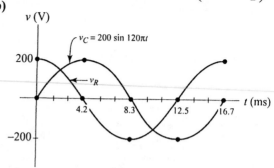

31. (a) 400 mA, −500 mA
(b) 1.1 ms, 5.6 ms
(c) 0 ms, 6.7 ms

32. (a) 120 V, −380 V
(b) 0 ms

CHAPTER 20 Trigonometry of Vectors

Exercise 20.1   Vectors and Phasors

1. $F = \sqrt{10^2 + 24^2} = 26$ N,

  Ref. angle $= \tan^{-1}\left(\dfrac{24}{10}\right) = 67° \rightarrow \theta = 67°$

2. 51 N, 149°

3. 59 ft/s, 154°

4. 15 m, 321°

5. 6.4×10^{-6} N, 231°

6. 500 N/C, 217°

7. $Z = \sqrt{33^2 + 22^2} \angle \tan^{-1}\left(\dfrac{22}{33}\right) = 40 \angle 34°$ kΩ

8. 1.9 ∠51° kΩ

9. $Z = \sqrt{2.4^2 + 4.7^2} \angle \tan^{-1}\left(\dfrac{-4.7}{2.4}\right) = 5.3 \angle{-63°}$ kΩ

10. 20 ∠−24° kΩ

11. $I = (24 - 12) \angle 90° = 12 \angle 90°$ V

12. 430 ∠−90° mA

13. 1.3 ∠−39° kΩ

14. 1.8 ∠60° kΩ

15. 300 ∠57° μA

16. 33 ∠−33° V

17. $Z_X = 3.1 \cos 65° + 6.1 \cos(-15°) = 7.20$

  $Z_Y = 3.1 \sin 65° + 6.1 \sin(-15°) = 1.23$

  $Z = \sqrt{7.20^2 + 1.23^2} \angle \tan^{-1}\left(\dfrac{1.23}{7.2}\right) = 7.3 \angle 9.7°$ kΩ

18. 6.7 ∠−20° kΩ

19. 20 ∠−21° kΩ

20. 33 ∠−11° kΩ

21. 46 N, 300°

22. 16 mi/h, 18°

23. $R_X = 5.5 + 2.0 \cos 40° = 7.03$,

  $R_Y = 2.0 \sin 40° = 1.29 \rightarrow R = 7.1$ mi, 10°

24. $V_X = 40 \cos(-45°) = 28.3$, $V_Y = 130 + 40 \sin(-45)$

  $= 102 \rightarrow 110 \angle 74° \rightarrow 110$ kn, 16° E of N

25. 71 ∠−62° V

26. 5.2 ∠−30° V

27. 86 ∠54° mA

28. 220 ∠66° μA

29. 18 ∠34° kΩ

30. 5.8 ∠−42° kΩ

31. 30 ∠−29° kΩ

32. 11 ∠−15° kΩ

33. $3.4 \times 10^3 \angle 169°$ N/C

34. $9.3 \times 10^{-6} \angle 27°$ T

Exercise 20.2   Law of Sines

1. $C = 40°$, $a = 7.5$, $c = 5.3$

2. $C = 65°$, $a = 3.5$, $c = 5.5$

3. $C = 83°$, $b = 29$, $c = 31$

4. $C = 66°$, $b = 15$, $c = 21$

5. $B = 45°$, $b = 6.5$, $c = 5.2$

6. $B = 40°$, $b = 7.4$, $c = 3.9$

7. $B = 75°$, $a = 34$, $b = 39$

8. $B = 70°$, $a = 25$, $b = 48$

9. $A = 42°$, $b = 21$, $c = 13$

10. $A = 24°$, $b = 60$, $c = 50$

11. $C = 75°$, $a = 2.2$, $b = 1.9$

12. $C = 86°$, $a = 4.6$, $b = 6.2$

13. $B = 63°$, $a = 4.2$, $c = 7.2$

14. $B = 65°$, $a = 4.6$, $c = 3.9$

15. $A = 20°$, $b = 68$, $c = 51$

16. $A = 73°$, $b = 17$, $c = 83$

17. $B = 47°$, $C = 66°$, $c = 5.0$

18. $B = 41°$, $C = 60°$, $c = 11$

19. $A = 47°$, $C = 46°$, $a = 630$

20. $A = 85°$, $C = 33°$, $a = 90$

21. $A = 51°$, $B = 24°$, $b = 0.24$

22. $A = 32°$, $B = 23°$, $b = 1.2$

23. $A = 19°$, $C = 10°$, $c = 5.7$

24. $A = 46°$, $C = 30°$, $c = 99$

25. $AB = 1500$ ft, $AC = 1200$ ft

26. tower A, 1.6 km

27. Let angle A be opposite F_1, angle B opposite F_2:

$$\frac{9.0 \times 10^{-6}}{\sin A} = \frac{13 \times 10^{-6}}{\sin 60°} \rightarrow A = 36.8°$$

and $B = 83.2° \rightarrow$

$$F_2 = \frac{13 \times 10^{-6}(\sin 83.2°)}{\sin 60°} = 15 \times 10^{-6} \text{ N}$$

28. 1.8×10^{-6} N

Exercise 20.3   Law of Cosines

1. $c = 7.1$, $A = 42°$, $B = 68°$

2. $c = 15$, $A = 41°$, $B = 84°$

3. $c = 81$, $A = 19°$, $B = 31°$

4. $c = 85$, $A = 48°$, $B = 22°$

5. $c = 2.6$, $A = 25°$, $B = 137°$

6. $c = 4.2$, $A = 124°$, $B = 34°$

7. $b = 0.42$, $A = 10°$, $C = 25°$

8. $b = 13$, $A = 22°$, $C = 131°$

9. $a = 0.44$, $B = 55°$, $C = 109°$

10. $a = 340$, $B = 30°$, $C = 40°$

11. $A = 29°$, $B = 47°$, $C = 104°$

12. $A = 25°$, $B = 48°$, $C = 107°$

13. $A = 62°$, $B = 73°$, $C = 45°$

14. $A = 93°$, $B = 48°$, $C = 39°$

15. $A = 130°$, $B = 26°$, $C = 24°$

16. $A = 131°$, $B = 23°$, $C = 26°$

17. $A = 67°$, $B = 67°$, $C = 46°$

18. $A = 29°$, $B = 122°$, $C = 29°$

19. $A = 39°$, $B = 58°$, $C = 83°$

20. $A = 52°$, $B = 105°$, $C = 23°$

21. $d_2 = 280^2 + 280^2 - 2(280)(280)\cos 108° \rightarrow d = 450$ m

22. Angle in triangle is $135°$.

$$d^2 = 5^2 + 6^2 - 2(5)(6)\cos 135° \rightarrow d = 10 \text{ mi}$$

23. $113°$, $41°$, $26°$

24. Add vectors: $F^2 = 1000^2 + 1000^2 - 2(1000)(1000)\cos 130° \rightarrow F = 1800$ lb

25. (a) 43 A
    (b) 23 A
    (c) $I_T = I_P \sqrt{3} = 1.73 I_P$

26. (a) $87°$
    (b) 7.0 mm^2

27. $Z_T^2 = 7.5^2 + 11^2 - 2(7.5)(11)\cos 130° \rightarrow$

$$Z_T = 16.8 \approx 17 \text{ k}\Omega, \frac{11}{\sin \theta} = \frac{16.8}{\sin 130°} \rightarrow \theta = 30°$$

28. 6.5 kΩ, $29°$

Review Exercises

1. 20 N, 37°

2. 94 N, 145°

3. 3.4 m/s, 199°

4. 75 N/C, 305°

5. 13 ∠−37° kΩ

6. 9.3 ∠62° kΩ

7. 150 ∠−90° mA

8. 12 ∠90° V

9. 13 ∠−21° kΩ

10. 34 ∠21° kΩ

11. $C = 20°$, $a = 7.2$, $c = 2.5$

12. $A = 30°$, $a = 3.1$, $b = 5.8$

13. $C = 66°$, $a = 19$, $b = 24$

14. $B = 86°$, $a = 280$, $c = 320$

15. $B = 49°$, $C = 91°$, $c = 17$

16. $A = 15°$, $B = 139°$, $b = 40$

17. $A = 29°$, $C = 54°$, $a = 4.1$

18. $A = 36°$, $C = 14°$, $c = 69$

19. $A = 43°$, $B = 27°$, $c = 25$

20. $A = 36°$, $B = 119°$, $c = 29$

21. $B = 42°$, $C = 78°$, $a = 13$

22. $A = 29°$, $C = 46°$, $b = 11$

23. $A = 39°$, $B = 57°$, $C = 84°$

24. $A = 26°$, $B = 41°$, $C = 113°$

25. $A = 122°$, $B = 18°$, $C = 40°$

26. $A = 65°$, $B = 78°$, $C = 37°$

27. 9.3 lb, 213°

28. 10 ∠90° + 6 ∠45° = 15 mi ∠73°

29. No: 86°, 50°, 44°

30. $\dfrac{80}{\sin(45° - \theta)} = \dfrac{220}{\sin 45°} \rightarrow 45° - \theta = 15° \rightarrow \theta = 30°$

31. **(a)** 26 ∠51° kΩ

    (b) 7.1 ∠−45° V

    (c) 29 ∠27° mA

32. 32 ∠1.8° kΩ

33. **(a)** 9.5 A

    (b) 9.2 A

34. 1.1mm, 49°, 31°

35. $Z^2 = 1.0^2 + 2.0^2 - 2(1.0)(2.0)\cos 25° = 1.37 \rightarrow$

$Z = 1.17 \approx 1.2$ kΩ, $\dfrac{2.0}{\sin \theta} = \dfrac{1.17}{\sin 25°} \rightarrow$

$\theta = 180 - 46° = 134°$, since θ must be the largest angle.

36. 810 Ω, 129°

CHAPTER 21   Complex Numbers and Phasors

Exercise 21.1   The *j* Operator

1. $j4$

2. $j3$

3. $j6$

4. $j10$

5. $j0.2$

6. $j0.5$

7. $j1.2$

8. $j1.1$

9. $j0.07$

10. $j0.09$

11. $j2$

12. $-j2$

13. $-j0.3$

14. $-j1.5$

15. $j2$

16. $-j4$

17. $j\sqrt{3}$

18. $j\sqrt{5}$

19. $j(2 \times 10^3)$

20. $j(4 \times 10^{-3})$

21. -12

22. -4

23. j

24. $j0.5$

25. 10

26. $-j4$

27. $j0.6$

28. -5

29. $-j800$

30. -225

31. $j(4 \times 10^3)$

32. -4.5×10^{-3}

33. $-j48$

34. 21

35. -1

36. $-j$

37. $-j3$

38. $j2.5$

39. $-j0.5$

40. $-j0.4$

41. $j0.5$

42. $j10$

43. $-j3$

44. $-j2$

45. 0.5

46. 0.75

47. $-j$

48. $j22$

49. $j150$

50. $-j4$

51. 35 V

52. -9.3 V

53. $-j220$ Ω

54. $j7.5$ mA

Exercise 21.2   Complex Numbers

1. $4 + j2$

2. $8 - j$

3. $0 + j5$

4. $-2 + j0$

5. $8.4 + j2.7$

6. $0.1 - j2.0$

7. $3 - j4$

8. $15 - j3$

9. $17 - j7$

10. $26 + j7$

11. $0 + j8$

12. $0 - j2$

13. $8.6 - j4.6$

14. $-0.2 + j1.6$

15. $61 + j0$

16. $53 + j0$

17. $39 + j54$

18. $6 + j18$

19. $-4 + j0$

20. $2 - j2$

21. $0.1 - j0.2$

22. $0.1 + j0.1$

23. $-1 + j3$

24. $1 - j5$

25. $1 - j$

26. $1 + j3$

27. $1 - j2$

28. $0.72 + j0.96$

29. $1.4 - j1.8$

30. $0.48 + j0.14$

31. $4.5 + j0.5$

32. $-1 + j0$

33. $1 - j0.5$

34. $0 - j$

35. $0 + j2.5$

36. $1 + j0.6$

37. $x^2 - x + jx - x - jx + 1 - j^2 = x^2 - 2x + 2$

38. $\left(\dfrac{1+j}{\sqrt{2}}\right)^2 = \dfrac{1 + j2 + j^2}{2} = \dfrac{2j}{2} = j$

39. $13.7 + j3.2$ kΩ

40. $1.7 + j7.8$ kΩ

41. $1.4 - j0.20$ kΩ

42. $14 + j2$ kΩ

43. $100 - j50$ V

44. $0.21 - j0.083$ A $= 210 - j83$ mA

Exercise 21.3   Complex Phasors

1.

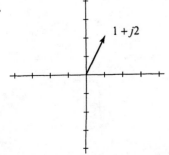

2.

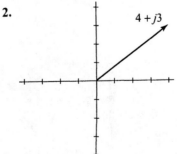

3.

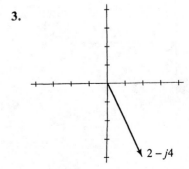

4.

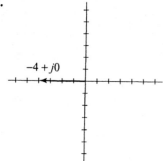

$5 - j6$

5.

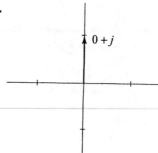

$0 + j$

6.

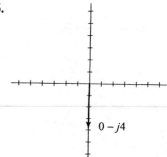

$0 - j4$

7.

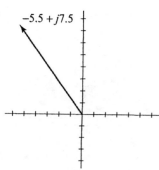

$-4 + j0$

8.

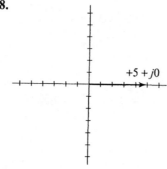

$+5 + j0$

9.

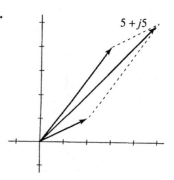

$-3.5 - j2.5$

10.

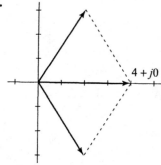

$-5.5 + j7.5$

11.

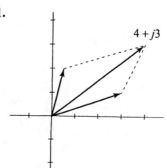

$4 + j3$

12.

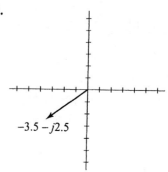

$5 + j5$

13.

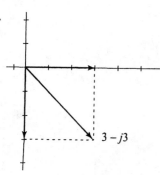

$4 + j0$

14.

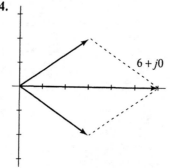

$6 + j0$

15.

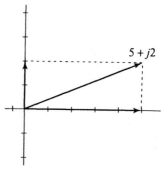

$5 + j2$

16.

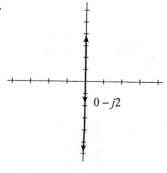

$3 - j3$

17.

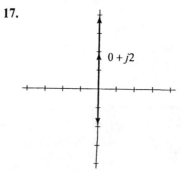

$0 + j2$

18.

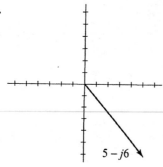

$0 - j2$

19.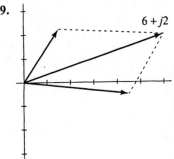

$6 + j2$

20.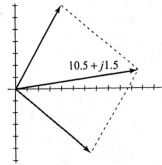

$10.5 + j1.5$

21. $\sqrt{2^2 + 2^2} \angle \tan^{-1}\left(\dfrac{2}{2}\right) = 2.8 \angle 45°$

22. $1.4 \angle 45°$

23. $4.5 \angle -63°$

24. $5.8 \angle -59°$

25. $1.4 \angle -45°$

26. $7.6 \angle -23°$

27. $4.5 \angle 27°$

28. $3.6 \angle 34°$

29. $55 \angle -90°$

30. $40 \angle 90°$

31. $75 \angle 0°$

32. $100 \angle 180°$

33. $25 \angle 53°$

34. $17 \angle 62°$

35. $1.3 \angle -67°$

36. $1.5 \angle -37°$

37. $3 \cos 45° + j(3 \sin 45°) = 2.1 + j2.1$

38. $2.5 + j4.3$

39. $43 - j25$

40. $42 - j15$

41. $100 + j0$

42. $60 + j0$

43. $0 - j10$

44. $0 - j75$

45. $2.9 - j1.4$

46. $0.60 + j4.3$

47. $0 + j15$

48. $0 + j9$

49. $7.1 - j7.1$

50. $14 - j14$

51. (a) $5.5 + j2.5 \text{ k}\Omega = 6.0 \angle 24° \text{ k}\Omega$
   (b) $3.3 - j4.7 \text{ k}\Omega = 5.7 \angle -55° \text{ k}\Omega$

52. (a) $1.6 \angle -45° \text{ k}\Omega = 1.1 - j1.1 \text{ k}\Omega$
   (b) $910 \angle 60° \text{ k}\Omega = 460 + j790 \text{ k}\Omega$

Exercise 21.4 Operations with Complex Phasors

1. $30 \cos 30° + j(\sin 30°) + 60 \cos 45° + j(60 \sin 45°)$
   $= 68.4 + j57.4 \rightarrow 89 \angle 40°$

2. $68 \angle 41°$

3. $32 \angle 64°$

4. $41 \angle 51°$

5. $97 \angle -8.1°$

6. $3.9 \angle 4.9°$

7. $10 \angle -90°$

8. $100 \angle 90°$

9. $6.4 \angle -30°$

10. $11 \angle 50°$

11. $5.7 \angle -76°$

12. $12 \angle -43°$

13. $2(4) \angle (40 + 20)° = 8 \angle 60°$

14. $50 \angle 60°$

15. $660 \angle -45°$

16. $450 \angle 20°$

17. $200 \angle -50°$

18. $72 \angle -58°$

19. $180 \angle 90°$

20. $240 \angle 0°$

21. $\left(\dfrac{60}{20}\right) \angle (70 - 20)° = 3.0 \angle 50°$

22. $5.0 \angle 20°$

23. $0.5 \angle -68°$

24. $0.2 \angle -60°$

25. $4.0 \angle 90°$

26. $12 \angle -90°$

27. $1.7 \angle 40°$

28. $3.5 \angle 18°$

29. $0.55 \angle 90°$

30. $1.3 \angle 68°$

31. $4 \angle 0°$

32. $25 \angle 16°$

33. $\dfrac{(12 + j9)(6 + j8)}{(6 - j8)(6 + j8)} = j1.5 \rightarrow 1.5 \angle 90°$

34. $1.6 \angle -72°$

35. $2.2 \angle -27°$

36. $2.2 \angle 27°$

37. $0.88 \angle 38°$

38. $0.88 \angle -38°$

39. $4.8 \angle 48°$ mA

40. $65 \angle -19°$ kΩ

41. $\left(\dfrac{12}{3.3}\right) \angle [50 - (-15)]° = 3.6 \angle 65°$ mA

42. $2.5 \angle -75°$ kΩ

43. $Z_T = \dfrac{(60 \angle 30°)(50 \angle 90°)}{60 \angle 30° + 50 \angle 90°} = \dfrac{(52 + j30)(j50)}{52 + j30 + j50} =$

$\dfrac{-1500 + j2600}{52 + j80} = \dfrac{3000 \angle 120°}{95.4 \angle 57°} = 31 \angle 63°$ kΩ

44. $131 \angle -23°$ kΩ

Review Exercises

1. $j9$

2. $j0.6$

3. $-j$

4. $-j0.1$

5. $-j1.6$

6. $j(8 \times 10^{-3})$

7. -32

8. 9

9. 96

10. -108

11. $-j72$

12. 2

13. $-j2.5$

14. $-j0.5$

15. 5

16. $-j6$

17. $6 + j2$

18. $10 - j6$

19. $22 - j7$

20. $-3 + j4$

21. $-2.1 - j4.1$

22. $-2 + j6$

23. $0.2 + j0.4$

24. $1 - j$

25. $2 - j4$

26. $0.28 + j0.96$

27. $1 + j0$

28. $0.69 + j0.54$

29. $3.2 \angle 72°$

30. $3.6 \angle -34°$

31. $45 \angle -90°$

32. $7 \angle 90°$

33. $87 + j50$

34. $3.5 + j3.5$

35. $0 + j5.5$

36. $0 - j6.8$

37. $8.9 \angle 39°$

38. $28 \angle 36°$

39. $40 \angle -31°$

40. $3.1 \angle -36°$

41. $3.0 \angle 90°$

42. $20 \angle -53°$

43. $14 \angle 40°$

44. $72 \angle -30°$

45. $60 \angle -70°$

46. $3.6 \angle 0°$

47. $3 \angle 20°$

48. $0.25 \angle -55°$

49. $3.0 \angle -8.0°$

50. $2.1 \angle 90°$

51. $1 + j0$

52. $13 \angle -23°$

53. **(a)** $22 \angle 56°$ V

   (b) $6.4 \angle -34°$ V

54. **(a)** $Y = \dfrac{1 \angle 0°}{20 \angle 45°} = \left(\dfrac{1}{20}\right)\angle[0 - (-45)]° =$

   $0.05 \angle 45°$ S $= 50 \angle 45°$ μS

   (b) $50 \angle -60°$ μS

55. **(a)** $75 \angle 60°$ V

   (b) $1.1 \angle -28°$ V

56. **(a)** $130 \angle -15°$ mA

   (b) $4.3 \angle 69°$ mA

57. $8.3 \angle 46°$ kΩ $= 5.8 + j6.0$ kΩ

58. $1.1 \angle 18°$ kΩ $= 1 + j0.33$ kΩ

CHAPTER 22   Series AC Circuits

Exercise 22.1   Inductive Reactance and *RL* Series Circuits

1. 3.8 kΩ

2. 4.7 kΩ

3. 630 Ω

4. 3.8 kΩ

5. 10 kΩ

6. 4.4 kΩ

7. 110 mH

8. 120 mH

9. 40 mH

10. 29 mH

11. 640 Hz

12. 1.3 kHz

13. 7.4 kHz

14. 5.4 kHz

15. 800 Ω

16. 15 kHz

17. 1.4 kΩ

18. 2.7 kΩ

19. 2.5 V

20. 24 V

21. 2.5 mA

22. 5.0 mA

23. $R + jX_L = 0.75 + j1.5$ kΩ $= 1.7 \angle 63°$ kΩ

24. $1.0 + j0.82$ kΩ $= 1.3 \angle 39°$ kΩ

25. $3.3 + j4.5$ kΩ $= 5.6 \angle 54°$ Ω

26. $6.8 + j3.9$ kΩ $= 7.8 \angle 30°$ kΩ

27. $2 + j1.2$ kΩ $= 2.3 \angle 31°$ kΩ

28. $1.5 + j1.5$ kΩ $= 2.1 \angle 45°$ kΩ

29. $910 + j750$ Ω $= 1.2 \angle 39°$ kΩ

30. $620 + j780$ Ω $= 1.0 \angle 52°$ kΩ

31. **(a)** $V_R = (0.020)(620) = 12.4 \approx 12$ V,

   $V_L = (0.020)(800) = 16$ V

   (b) $V_T = V_R + jV_L = 12.4 + j16$ V $= 20 \angle 52°$ V,

   $Z = 620 + j800$ Ω $= 1.0 \angle 52°$ kΩ

32. **(a)** $V_R = 34$ V, $V_L = 45$ V

   (b) $V_T = 56 \angle 53°$ V, $Z = 1.1 \angle 53°$ kΩ

33. **(a)** $V_R = 5$ V, $V_L = 7.5$ V

   (b) $V_T = 9.0 \angle 56°$ V, $Z = 1.8 \angle 56°$ kΩ

34. **(a)** $V_R = 20$ V, $V_L = 12$ V

   (b) $V_T = 23 \angle 31°$ V, $Z = 6.5 \angle 31°$ kΩ

35. **(a)** $V_R = 17$ V, $V_L = 14$ V

   (b) $V_T = 21 \angle 39°$ V, $Z = 28 \angle 39°$ kΩ

36. **(a)** $V_R = 13$ V, $V_L = 13$ V

   (b) $V_T = 19 \angle 45°$ V, $Z = 23 \angle 45°$ kΩ

37. **(a)** $V_R = 41$ V, $V_L = 33$ V

    (b) $V_T = 52 \angle 39°$ V, $Z = 3.5 \angle 39°$ kΩ

38. **(a)** $V_R = 9.5$ V, $V_L = 3.1$ V

    (b) $V_T = 10 \angle 18°$ V, $Z = 2.8 \angle 18°$ kΩ

39. **(a)** $Z = 620 + j330 = 700 \angle 28°$ Ω

    (b) $I = \dfrac{V_T}{Z} = \dfrac{15}{700} = 21$ mA,

       $V_R = IR = (0.021)(620) = 13$ V,

       $V_L = IX_L = (0.020)(330) = 7.1$ V

40. **(a)** $580 \angle 59°$ Ω

    (b) $I = 34$ mA, $V_R = 9.9$ V, $V_L = 17$ V

41. **(a)** $3.2 \angle 18°$ kΩ

    (b) $I = 3.8$ mA, $V_R = 11$ V, $V_L = 3.8$ V

42. **(a)** $5.0 \angle 69°$ kΩ

    (b) $I = 3.2$ mA, $V_R = 5.7$ V, $V_L = 15$ V

43. **(a)** $4.9 \angle 29°$ kΩ

    (b) $I = 12$ mA, $V_R = 52$ V, $V_L = 29$ V

44. **(a)** $11 \angle 59°$ kΩ

    (b) $I = 820$ μA, $V_R = 4.6$ V, $V_L = 7.8$ V

45. **(a)** $16 \angle 45°$ kΩ

    (b) $I = 3.2$ mA, $V_R = 35$ V, $V_L = 35$ V

46. **(a)** $17 \angle 27°$ kΩ

    (b) $I = 1.2$ mA, $V_R = 18$ V, $V_L = 9.0$ V

47. **(a)** $X_L = 2\pi(1500)(0.150) = 1414$ Ω ≈ 1.4 kΩ,

       $I = \dfrac{7.5}{1414} = 5.3$ mA, $R = \sqrt{(2.3)^2 - (1.414)^2}$

       $= 1.814 \approx 1.8$ kΩ, $V_R = 9.6$ V

    (b) $V_T = 9.6 + j7.5 = 12 \angle 38°$ V

48. **(a)** $L = 1.1$ H, $I = 830$ μA, $V_L = 4.6$ V

    (b) $V_T = 11 \angle 25°$ V, $Z = 13 \angle 25°$ kΩ

49. **(a)** $X_L = 280$ Ω, $I = 400$ mA, $V_R = 40$ V, $V_L = 110$ V

    (b) $Z = 300 \angle 71°$ Ω

50. **(a)** $I = 330$ mA, $V_L = 110$ V, $X_L = 330$ Ω, $L = 870$ mH

    (b) $Z = 360 \angle 65°$ Ω

Exercise 22.2 Capacitive Reactance and *RC* Series Circuits

1. 1.3 kΩ

2. 640 Ω

3. 21 kΩ

4. 20 kΩ

5. 530 Ω

6. 400 Ω

7. 1.6 nF

8. 830 pF

9. 99 nF

10. 56 nF

11. 1.3 kHz

12. 3.2 kHz

13. 13 kHz

14. 71 kHz

15. 1.7 kΩ

16. 650 Ω

17. 8.0 kΩ

18. 9.9 kΩ

19. 4.8 V

20. 5.6 V

21. 400 μA

22. 22 mA

23. $1.6 - j1.2$ kΩ $= 2.0 \angle{-37°}$ kΩ

24. $8.2 - j16$ kΩ $= 18 \angle{-63°}$ kΩ

25. $680 - j910$ Ω $= 1.1 \angle{-53°}$ kΩ

26. $3.3 - j2.2$ kΩ $= 4.0 \angle{-34°}$ kΩ

27. $550 - j550$ Ω $= 780 \angle{-45°}$ Ω

28. $1.5 - j0.75$ kΩ $= 1.7 \angle{-27°}$ kΩ

29. $0.82 - j1.0$ kΩ $= 1.3 \angle{-51°}$ kΩ

30. $710 - j650$ Ω $= 960 \angle{-42°}$ Ω

31. **(a)** $V_R = (0.0032)(7500) = 24$ V,

       $V_C = (0.0032)(4000) = 13$ V

    (b) $V_T = V_R - jV_C = 24 - j13 = 27 \angle{-28°}$ V,

       $Z = 77.5 - j4.0$ kΩ $= 8.5 \angle{-28°}$ kΩ

32. **(a)** $V_R = 38$ V, $V_C = 48$ V

    (b) $V_T = 61 \angle{-51°}$ V, $Z = 19 \angle{-51°}$ kΩ

33. **(a)** $V_R = 5.0$ V, $V_C = 13$ V

    (b) $V_T = 13 \angle{-68°}$ V, $Z = 27 \angle{-68°}$ kΩ

34. **(a)** $V_R = 16$ V, $V_C = 6.5$ V

    (b) $V_T = 17 \angle{-23°}$ V, $Z = 26 \angle{-23°}$ kΩ

35. **(a)** $V_R = 2.0$ V, $V_C = 3.2$ V

    (b) $V_T = 3.8 \angle{-58°}$ V, $Z = 940 \angle{-58°}$ Ω

36. **(a)** $V_R = 2.5$ V, $V_C = 1.9$ V

    (b) $V_T = 3.2 \angle{-38°}$ V, $Z = 780 \angle{-38°}$ Ω

37. (a) $V_R = 28$ V, $V_C = 18$ V
    (b) $V_T = 33 \angle{-32°}$ V, $Z = 5.1 \angle{-32°}$ kΩ
38. (a) $V_R = 30$ V, $V_C = 60$ V
    (b) $V_T = 67 \angle{-63°}$ V, $Z = 2.7 \angle{-63°}$ kΩ
39. (a) $Z = 920 \angle{-42°}$ Ω
    (b) $I = 22$ mA, $V_R = 15$ V, $V_C = 13$ V
40. (a) $Z = 780 \angle{-53°}$ Ω
    (b) $I = 11$ mA, $V_R = 5.1$ V, $V_C = 6.7$ V
41. (a) $Z = 1.5 \angle{-35°}$ Ω
    (b) $I = 16$ mA, $V_R = 20$ V, $V_C = 14$ V
42. (a) $Z = 8.3 \angle{-48°}$ kΩ
    (b) $I = 2.9$ mA, $V_R = 16$ V, $V_C = 18$ V
43. (a) $Z = 15 \angle{-58°}$ kΩ
    (b) $I = 780$ μA, $V_R = 6.4$ V, $V_C = 10$ V
44. (a) $Z = 36 \angle{-56°}$ kΩ
    (b) $I = 280$ μA, $V_R = 5.6$ V, $V_C = 8.3$ V
45. (a) $Z = 1.1 \angle{-45°}$ Ω
    (b) $I = 9.1$ mA, $V_R = 6.9$ V, $V_C = 6.9$ V

46. (a) $Z = 1.2 \angle{-67°}$ Ω
    (b) $I = 10$ mA, $V_R = 4.7$ V, $V_C = 11$ V
47. (a) $X_C = \dfrac{1}{2\pi(1000)(100 \times 10^{-9})} = 1.59 \approx 1.6$ kΩ,

    Using result for Z in (b) below:

    $$I = \frac{V}{Z} = \frac{15}{3660} = 4.1 \text{ mA}$$
    $$V_C = (0.0041)(1590) = 6.5 \text{ V}$$
    $$V_R = (0.0041)(3300) = 14 \text{ V}$$

    (b) $Z = 3.3 - j1.59$ kΩ $= 3.66 \angle{-26°}$ kΩ
    $\approx 3.7 \angle{-26°}$ kΩ
48. (a) $X_C = 2.3$ kΩ, $V_R = 7.8$ V
    (b) $V_T = 23 \angle{-71°}$ V, $Z = 2.5 \angle{-71°}$ kΩ
49. (a) $X_C = 18$ kΩ, $V_R = 94$ V, $V_C = 76$ V, $I = 4.3$ mA
    (b) $Z = 28 \angle{-39°}$ kΩ
50. (a) $R = 300$ Ω, $C = 5.9$ μF, $I = 220$ mA, $V_R = 66$ V
    (b) $Z = 540 \angle{-56°}$ Ω

Exercise 22.3   *RLC* Series Circuits and Resonance

1. $X = |800 - 500| = 300$ Ω,
   $Z = 750 + j300$ Ω $= 810 \angle{22°}$ Ω

2. $X = 300$ Ω, $Z = 750 - j300$ Ω $= 810 \angle{-22°}$ Ω

3. $X = 2.2$ kΩ, $Z = 1.8 - j2.2$ kΩ $= 2.8 \angle{-51°}$ kΩ

4. $X = 2.0$ kΩ, $Z = 3.0 + j2.0$ kΩ $= 3.6 \angle{34°}$ kΩ

5. $X = 4.8$ kΩ, $Z = 3.9 + j4.8$ kΩ $= 6.2 \angle{51°}$ kΩ

6. $X = 6.0$ kΩ, $Z = 5.1 - j6.0$ kΩ $= 7.9 \angle{-50°}$ kΩ

7. $X = 450$ Ω, $Z = 1000 - j450$ Ω $= 1100 \angle{-24°}$ Ω

8. $X = 370$ Ω, $Z = 680 + j370$ Ω $= 770 \angle{29°}$ Ω

9. $X = 350$ Ω, $Z = 200 + j350$ Ω $= 400 \angle{60°}$ Ω

10. $X = 620$ Ω, $Z = 200 - j620$ Ω $= 650 \angle{-72°}$ Ω

11. $Z = 3.3 + j(1.2 - 4.7) = 3.3 - j3.5$ kΩ $= 4.81 \angle{-47°}$ kΩ,

    $$I = \frac{V}{Z} = \frac{12}{4.81} = 2.5 \text{ mA}, \quad V_R = 2.5(3.3) = 8.3 \text{ V},$$

    $V_L = 2.5(1.2) = 3.0$ V, $V_C = 2.5(4.7) = 12$ V,

    $V_T = 8.3 + j(3.0 - 12)$ V $= 12 \angle{-47°}$ V

12. $I = 8.0$ mA, $V_R = 24$ V, $V_L = 12$ V, $V_C = 9.5$ V,
    $V_T = 24 \angle{5.7°}$ V

13. $I = 72$ mA, $V_R = 20$ V, $V_L = 37$ V, $V_C = 33$ V,
    $V_T = 20 \angle{13°}$ V

14. $I = 22$ mA, $V_R = 15$ V, $V_L = 14$ V, $V_C = 17$ V,
    $V_T = 15 \angle{-10°}$ V

15. $I = 4.8$ mA, $V_R = 4.3$ V, $V_L = 20$ V, $V_C = 7.1$ V,
    $V_T = 14 \angle{72°}$ V

16. $I = 680$ μA, $V_R = 7.5$ V, $V_L = 5.4$ V, $V_C = 8.2$ V,
    $V_T = 8.0 \angle{-20°}$ V

17. $I = 43$ mA, $V_R = 26$ V, $V_L = 51$ V, $V_C = 36$ V,
    $V_T = 30 \angle{31°}$ V

18. $I = 13$ mA, $V_R = 6.4$ V, $V_L = 12$ V, $V_C = 13$ V,
    $V_T = 6.5 \angle{-9.1°}$ V

19. 3.6 kHz

20. 2.3 kHz

21. 28 kHz

22. 27 kHz

23. 1.5 μF

24. 470 pF

25. 70 mH

26. 41 mH

27. (a) $X_L = 2\pi(2600)(0.050) = 817 \approx 820\ \Omega$,

$$X_C = \frac{1}{2\pi(2600)(100 \times 10^{-6})} = 612 \approx 610\ \Omega,$$

$Z = 330 + j305 \approx 330 + j210\ \Omega = 390\ \angle 32°\ \Omega$

(b) $I = \dfrac{12}{390} = 31\ \text{mA},\ V_R = (0.031)(330) = 10\ \text{V}$,

$V_L = (0.031)(817) = 25\ \text{V},\ V_C = (0.031)(612) = 19\ \text{V}$,

$V_T = 10 + j6\ \text{V} = 12\ \angle 32°\ \text{V}$

28. (a) $X_L = 1.9\ \text{k}\Omega,\ X_C = 2.7\ \text{k}\Omega,\ Z = 1000 - j770\ \Omega$
$= 1.3\ \angle -38°\ \text{k}\Omega$

(b) $I = 19\ \text{mA},\ V_R = 19\ \text{V},\ V_L = 36\ \text{V},\ V_C = 50\ \text{V}$,
$V_T = 19 - j14\ \text{V} = 24\ \angle -38°\ \text{V}$

29. (a) $Z = 600 + j450\ \Omega = 750\ \angle 37°\ \Omega$

(b) $I = 27\ \text{mA},\ P = 430\ \text{mW},\ Q = 320\ \text{mVAR}$,
$S = 540\ \text{mVI, p.f.} = 0.80$

30. (a) $Z = 1 - j2.5\ \text{k}\Omega = 2.7\ \angle -68°\ \text{k}\Omega$

(b) $I = 3.7\ \text{mA},\ P = 14\ \text{mW},\ Q = 34\ \text{mVAR}$,
$S = 37\ \text{mVI, p.f.} = 0.375$

31. (a) $V_R = 18\ \text{V},\ V_L = 36\ \text{V},\ V_C = 16\ \text{V}$,
$V_T = 18 + j20\ \text{V} = 27\ \angle 48°\ \text{V}$

(b) $Z = 1.8 + j2.0\ \text{k}\Omega = 2.7\ \angle 48°\ \text{k}\Omega$

32. (a) $I = 9.8\ \text{mA},\ V_L = 3.5\ \text{V},\ V_C = 7.4\ \text{V}$,
$V_T = 5.0 - j3.8\ \text{V} = 6.3\ \angle -37°\ \text{V}$

(b) $Z = 510 - j390\ \Omega = 640\ \angle -37°\ \Omega$

33. (a) $X_L = 1.9\ \text{k}\Omega,\ X_C = 3.2\ \text{k}\Omega$,
$Z = 3.9 - j1.3\ \text{k}\Omega = 4.1\ \angle -18°\ \text{k}\Omega$

(b) $I = 2.4\ \text{mA},\ V_{R_1} = 6.6\ \text{V},\ V_{R_2} = 2.9\ \text{V},\ V_L = 4.6\ \text{V}$,
$V_C = 7.7\ \text{V},\ V_T = 9.5 - j3.2\ \text{V} = 10\ \angle -18°\ \text{V}$

34. (a) $X_L = 650\ \Omega,\ X_C = 1.5\ \text{k}\Omega$,
$Z = 510 - j880\ \Omega = 1.0\ \angle -60°\ \text{k}\Omega$

(b) $I = 18\ \text{mA},\ V_{R_1} = 6.5\ \text{V},\ V_{R_2} = 3.5\ \text{V},\ V_L = 13\ \text{V},\ V_C$
$= 30\ \text{V},\ V_T = 10 - j17\ \text{V} = 20\ \angle -60°\ \text{V}$

Review Exercises

1. $9.4\ \text{k}\Omega$

2. $260\ \Omega$

3. $760\ \Omega$

4. $2.3\ \text{k}\Omega$

5. $2.0\ \text{kHz}$

6. $190\ \text{mH}$

7. $4.0\ \text{nF}$

8. $940\ \text{Hz}$

9. $16\ \text{kHz}$

10. $1.0\ \text{kHz}$

11. $820 + j1000\ \Omega = 1.3\ \angle 51°\ \text{k}\Omega$

12. $3.3 + j1.8\ \text{k}\Omega = 3.8\ \angle 29°\ \text{k}\Omega$

13. $150 + j430\ \Omega = 460\ \angle 71°\ \Omega$

14. $1.0 + j0.64\ \text{k}\Omega = 1.2\ \angle 33°\ \text{k}\Omega$

15. $6.2 - j8.5\ \text{k}\Omega = 11\ \angle -54°\ \text{k}\Omega$

16. $7.5 - j5.0\ \text{k}\Omega = 9.0\ \angle -34°\ \text{k}\Omega$

17. $1800 - j780\ \Omega = 2.0\ \angle -23°\ \text{k}\Omega$

18. $330 - j440\ \Omega = 550\ \angle -53°\ \Omega$

19. $470 + j550\ \Omega = 720\ \angle 49°\ \Omega$

20. $1.1 - j0.60\ \text{k}\Omega = 1.3\ \angle -29°\ \text{k}\Omega$

21. $6.8 - j3.1\ \text{k}\Omega = 7.5\ \angle -25°$

22. $560 + j1200\ \Omega = 1.3\ \angle 65°\ \text{k}\Omega$

23. (a) $Z = 730\ \angle 58°\ \Omega$

(b) $I = 20\ \text{mA},\ V_T = 8.0 + j13\ \text{V} = 15\ \angle 58°\ \text{V}$

24. (a) $Z = 6.8\ \angle 6.3°\ \text{k}\Omega$

(b) $I = 2.0\ \text{mA},\ V_T = 14 + j1.5\ \text{V} = 14\ \angle 6.3°\ \text{V}$

25. (a) $Z = 8.4\ \angle -42°\ \Omega$

(b) $I = 2.9\ \text{mA},\ V_T = 18 - j16\ \text{V} = 24\ \angle -42°\ \text{V}$

26. (a) $Z = 14\ \angle -72°\ \text{k}\Omega$

(b) $I = 620\ \mu\text{A},\ V_T = 2.7 - j8.1\ \text{V} = 8.5\ \angle -72°\ \text{V}$

27. (a) $Z = 4.8\ \angle 47°\ \text{k}\Omega$

(b) $I = 2.5\ \text{mA},\ V_T = 8.2 + j8.7\ \text{V} = 12\ \angle 47°\ \text{V}$

28. (a) $Z = 1.0\ \angle -36°\ \text{k}\Omega$

(b) $I = 35\ \text{mA},\ V_T = 29 - j21\ \text{V} = 36\ \angle -36°\ \text{V}$

29. (a) $X_L = 1.1\ \text{k}\Omega,\ V_R = 18\ \text{V},\ V_L = 11\ \text{V}$

(b) $V_T = 18 + j11\ \text{V} = 21\ \angle 31°\ \text{V}$,
$Z = 1.8 + j1.1\ \text{k}\Omega = 2.1\ \angle 31°\ \text{k}\Omega$

30. (a) $X_L = 20\ \text{k}\Omega,\ V_R = 7.1\ \text{V},\ V_L = 7.1\ \text{V},\ I = 360\ \mu\text{A}$

(b) $V_T = 7.1 + j7.1\ \text{V} = 10\ \angle 45°\ \text{V}$,
$Z = 20 + j20\ \text{k}\Omega = 28\ \angle 45°\ \text{k}\Omega$

31. (a) $X_C = 4.6\ \text{k}\Omega,\ V_R = 2.6\ \text{V},\ V_C = 3.7\ \text{V}$

(b) $V_T = 2.6 - j3.7\ \text{V} = 4.5\ \angle -54°\ \text{V}$,
$Z = 3.3 - j4.6\ \text{k}\Omega = 5.7\ \angle -54°\ \text{k}\Omega$

32. (a) $X_C = 640\ \Omega,\ V_R = 6.2\ \text{V},\ V_C = 7.8\ \text{V},\ I = 12\ \text{mA}$

(b) $V_T = 6.2 - j7.8 = 10\ \angle -51°\ \text{V}$,
$Z = 510 - j640\ \Omega = 820\ \angle -51°\ \Omega$

33. (a) $X_L = 5.7\ \text{k}\Omega,\ X_C = 2.7\ \text{k}\Omega,\ V_R = 23\ \text{V}$,
$V_L = 43\ \text{V},\ V_C = 20\ \text{V},\ I = 7.5\ \text{mA}$

(b) $V_T = 23 + j23\ \text{V} = 32\ \angle 45°\ \text{V}$,
$Z = 3.0 + j3.0\ \text{k}\Omega = 4.2\ \angle 45°\ \text{k}\Omega$

34. (a) $X_L = 6.3$ kΩ, $X_C = 11$ kΩ, $V_R = 34$ V, $V_L = 35$ V, $V_C = 58$ V
    (b) $V_T = 34 - j24$ V $= 42 \angle{-35°}$ V, $Z = 6.2 - j4.3$ kΩ $= 7.6 \angle{-35°}$ kΩ

35. (a) $Z = 680 + j(1200 - 500 - 1600) = 680 - j900$ Ω $= 1.13 \angle{-53°}$ Ω $\approx 1.1 \angle{-53°}$ Ω, $I = \dfrac{9.0}{1130} = 8.0$ mA

    (b) $\dot{V}_R = (0.008)(680) = 5.4$ V, $V_L = (0.008)(1.2) = 9.6$ V, $V_C = (0.008)(500 + 1600) = 16.8$ V ≈ 17 V,
    $V_T = 54. + j(9.6 - 16.8) = 5.4 - j7.2$ V $= 9.0 \angle{-53°}$ V, $P = (0.008)^2(680) = 43$ mW

36. (a) $V_T = 28 + j17$ V $= 33 \angle{31°}$ V, $Z = 5.6 + j3.3$ kΩ $= 6.5 \angle{31°}$ kΩ
    (b) $P = 140$ mW

CHAPTER 23 Parallel AC Circuits

Exercise 23.1 *RL* Circuits

1. $I_R = \dfrac{12}{7500} = 1.60$ mA, $I_L = \dfrac{12}{6500} = 1.84$ mA, $I_T = 1.60 - j1.84$ mA $\approx 1.6 - j1.8$ mA,

   $I_T = 2.44 \angle{-49°} \approx 2.4 \angle{-49°}$ mA, $Z = \dfrac{12}{2.44 \angle{-49°}} = 4.9 \angle{49°}$ kΩ $= 3.2 + j3.7$ kΩ

2. $I_T = 11 - j4.1$ mA $= 11 \angle{-21°}$ mA, $Z = 1300 + 500$ Ω $= 1.4 \angle{21°}$ kΩ

3. $I_T = 4.2 - j6.1$ mA $= 7.4 \angle{-56°}$ mA, $Z = 380 + j560$ Ω $= 680 \angle{56°}$ Ω

4. $I_T = 9.9 - j6.9$ mA $= 12 \angle{-35°}$ mA, $Z = 610 + j430$ Ω $= 750 \angle{35°}$ Ω

5. $I_T = 2.0 - j2.0$ mA $= 2.8 \angle{-45°}$ mA, $Z = 5.0 + j5.0$ kΩ $= 7.1 \angle{45°}$ kΩ

6. $I_T = 53 - j53$ mA $= 75 \angle{-45°}$ mA, $Z = 225 + j225$ Ω $= 318 \angle{45°}$ Ω

7. $I_T = 25 - j18$ mA $= 31 \angle{-35°}$ mA, $Z = 340 + j240$ Ω $= 420 \angle{35°}$ Ω

8. $I_T = 5.6 - j7.4$ mA $= 9.3 \angle{-53°}$ mA, $Z = 300 + j400$ kΩ $= 490 \angle{53°}$ kΩ

9. (a) $I_R = 1.1$ mA, $I_L = 1.4$ mA
   (b) $I_T = 1.1 - j1.4$ mA $= 1.8 \angle{-52°}$ mA, $Z = 2.1 + j2.7$ kΩ $= 3.4 \angle{52°}$ kΩ

10. (a) $V = 5.4$ V, $I_L = 730$ μA
    (b) $I_T = 800 - j730$ μA $= 1.1 \angle{-42°}$ mA, $Z = 3.7 + j3.4$ kΩ $= 5.0 \angle{42°}$ kΩ

11. (a) $X_L = 2\pi(10,000)(0.30) = 18.8$ kΩ $\rightarrow I_T = \dfrac{12}{24,000} - \dfrac{j12}{18,800} = 500 - j638$ μA $\approx 500 - j640$ μA

    $I_T = 811 \angle{-52°} \approx 810 \angle{-52°}$ μA

    (b) $Z = \dfrac{12 \angle{0°} \text{ V}}{811 \angle{-52°} \text{ μA}} = 14.8 \angle{52°}$ kΩ $\approx 15 \angle{52°}$ kΩ

    $Z = 9.1 + j12$ kΩ $\rightarrow R = 9.1$ kΩ, $X_L = 12$ kΩ and $L = 190$ mH

12. (a) $I_T = 22 - j25$ mA $= 34 \angle{-49°}$ mA, $Z = 780 + j890$ Ω $= 1.2 \angle{49°}$ kΩ
    (b) $R = 780$ Ω, $X_L = 890$ Ω, and $L = 57$ mH

13. (a) $I_T = 6.1 - j5.5$ mA $= 8.2 \angle{-42°}$ mA
    (b) $Z = 3.8 + j3.4$ kΩ $= 5.0 \angle{42°}$ kΩ, $R = 3.8$ kΩ, $X_L = 3.4$ kΩ, and $L = 90$ mH

14. (a) $I_T = 6.2 - j3.9$ mA $= 7.3 \angle{-32°}$ mA
    (b) $Z = 340 + j210$ Ω $= 400 \angle{32°}$ Ω, $R = 340$ Ω, $X_L = 210$ Ω, and $L = 2.8$ mH

Exercise 23.2 *RC* Circuits

1. $I_R = \dfrac{25}{3000} = 8.33$ mA, $I_C = \dfrac{25}{2000} = 12.5$ mA $\rightarrow$

   $I_T \approx 8.3 + j13$ mA $= 15.0 \angle 56.3°$ mA $\approx 15 \angle 56°$ mA

   $Z = \dfrac{25 \angle 0°}{15 \angle 56°} = 1.67 \angle{-56°}$ kΩ $\approx 1.7 \angle{-56°}$ kΩ $= 0.92 - j1.4$ kΩ

2. $I_T = 3.6 + j2.4$ mA $= 4.3 \angle 34°$ mA, $Z = 3.8 - j2.6$ kΩ $= 4.6 \angle{-34°}$ kΩ

3. $I_T = 48 + j64$ mA $= 80 \angle 53°$ mA, $Z = 230 - j300$ Ω $= 370 \angle{-53°}$ Ω

4. $I_T = 18 + j13$ mA $= 22 \angle 36°$ mA, $Z = 370 - j270$ Ω $= 450 \angle{-36°}$ Ω

5. $I_T = 800 + j510$ μA $= 950 \angle 33°$ μA, $Z = 21 - j14$ kΩ $= 25 \angle{-33°}$ kΩ

6. $I_T = 690 + j820$ μA $= 1.1 \angle 50°$ mA, $Z = 5.4 - j6.4$ kΩ $= 8.4 \angle{-50°}$ kΩ

7. $I_T = 20 + j15$ mA $= 25 \angle 37°$ mA, $Z = 480 - j360$ Ω $= 600 \angle{-37°}$ Ω

8. $I_T = 15 + j25$ mA $= 29 \angle 60°$ mA, $Z = 270 - j470$ Ω $= 550 \angle{-60°}$ Ω

9. (a) $I_R = 7.1$ mA, $I_C = 13$ mA, $I_T = 7.1 + j13$ mA $= 14 \angle 60°$ mA
   (b) $Z = 520 - j900$ Ω $= 1.0 \angle{-60°}$ kΩ

10. (a) $V = 12$ V, $I_R = 1.5$ mA, $I_T = 1.5 + j2.2$ mA $= 2.7 \angle 56°$ mA
    (b) $Z = 2.6 - j3.8$ kΩ $= 4.6 \angle{-56°}$ kΩ

11. (a) $X_C = \dfrac{1}{2\pi(15{,}000)(25 \times 10^{-9})} = 424$ Ω

    $V = V_C = IX_C = (0.0095)(424) = 4.03$ V ≈ 4.0 V

    $I_R = \dfrac{4.03}{680} = 5.9$ mA

    $I_T = 5.9 + j9.5$ mA $= 11.2 \angle 58.0°$ mA

    $I_T \approx 11 \angle 58°$ mA

    (b) $Z = \dfrac{V}{I_T} = \dfrac{4.03 \angle 0°}{0.0112 \angle 58°} \approx 360 \angle{-58°}$ Ω $= 190 - j305$ Ω $\approx 190 - j310$ Ω $\rightarrow$

    $R = 190$ Ω, $X_C = 310$ Ω, and $C = 35$ nF

12. (a) $V = 6.1$ V, $I_C = 920$ μA, $I_T = 900 + j920$ μA $= 1.3 \angle 46°$ mA
    (b) $Z = 3.3 - j3.4$ kΩ $= 4.7 \angle{-46°}$ kΩ
    $R = 3.3$ kΩ, $X_C = 3.4$ kΩ, and $C = 1.6$ nF

13. (a) $I_R = 29$ mA, $I_C = 23$ mA, $I_T = 29 + j23$ mA $= 37 \angle 38°$ mA
    (b) $Z = 390 - j300$ Ω $= 490 \angle{-38°}$ Ω
    $R = 390$ Ω, $X_C = 300$ Ω, and $C = 100$ nF

14. (a) $I_R = 2.5$ mA, $I_C = 377$ μA, $I_T = 2.5 + j0.38$ mA $= 2.5 \angle 8.6°$ mA
    (b) $Z = 2.3 - j0.35$ kΩ $= 2.4 \angle{-8.6°}$ kΩ
    $R = 2.3$ kΩ, $X_C = 350$ Ω, and $C = 22$ nF

Exercise 23.3 Susceptance and Admittance

1. $G = \dfrac{1}{7500} = 130$ μS, $B = \dfrac{1}{6500} = 150$ μS $\rightarrow Y = 130 - j150$ μS $= 200 \angle{-49°}$ μS

2. $G = 670$ μS, $B = 260$ μS, $Y = 670 - j260$ μS $= 710 \angle{-21°}$ μS

3. $G = 830 \ \mu\text{S}, B = 1.2 \ \text{mS},$
$Y = 0.83 - j1.2 \ \text{mS} = 1.5 \ \angle{-56°} \ \text{mS}$

4. $G = 1.1 \ \text{mS}, B = 770 \ \mu\text{S},$
$Y = 1.1 - j0.77 \ \text{mS} = 1.3 \ \angle{-35°} \ \text{mS}$

5. $G = 100 \ \mu\text{S}, B = 100 \ \mu\text{S},$
$Y = 100 - j100 \ \mu\text{S} = 140 \ \angle{-45°} \ \mu\text{S}$

6. $G = 2.2 \ \text{mS}, B = 2.2 \ \text{mS},$
$Y = 2.2 - j2.2 \ \text{mS} = 3.1 \ \angle{-45°} \ \text{mS}$

7. $G = 2.0 \ \text{mS}, B = 1.4 \ \text{mS},$
$Y = 2.0 - j1.4 \ \text{mS} = 2.4 \ \angle{-35°} \ \text{mS}$

8. $G = 1.2 \ \text{mS}, B = 1.6 \ \text{mS},$
$Y = 1.2 - j1.6 \ \text{mS} = 2.0 \ \angle{-53°} \ \text{mS}$

9. $G = \dfrac{1}{3000} = 330 \ \mu\text{S}, \ B = \dfrac{1}{2000} = 500 \ \mu\text{S} \rightarrow$
$Y = 330 + j500 \ \mu\text{S} = 600 \ \angle{-56°} \ \mu\text{S}$

10. $G = 180 \ \mu\text{S}, B = 120 \ \mu\text{S},$
$Y = 180 + j120 \ \mu\text{S} = 220 \ \angle{34°} \ \mu\text{S}$

11. $G = 1.6 \ \text{mS}, B = 2.1 \ \text{mS},$
$Y = 1.6 + j2.1 \ \text{mS} = 2.7 \ \angle{53°} \ \text{mS}$

12. $G = 1.8 \ \text{mS}, B = 1.3 \ \text{mS},$
$Y = 1.8 + j1.3 \ \text{mS} = 2.2 \ \angle{36°} \ \mu\text{S}$

13. $G = 33 \ \mu\text{S}, B = 21 \ \mu\text{S},$
$Y = 33 + j21 \ \mu\text{S} = 40 \ \angle{33°} \ \mu\text{S}$

14. $G = 77 \ \mu\text{S}, B = 91 \ \mu\text{S},$
$Y = 77 + j91 \ \mu\text{S} = 120 \ \angle{50°} \ \mu\text{S}$

15. $G = 1.3 \ \text{mS}, B = 1.0 \ \text{mS},$
$Y = 1.3 + j1.0 \ \text{mS} = 1.7 \ \angle{37°} \ \mu\text{S}$

16. $G = 910 \ \mu\text{S}, B = 1.6 \ \mu\text{S},$
$Y = 0.91 + j1.6 \ \text{mS} = 1.8 \ \angle{60°} \ \text{mS}$

17. (a) $X_L = 2\pi(10,000)(0.300) = 18.8 \ \text{k}\Omega$

$G = \dfrac{1}{24,000} = 41.7 \ \mu\text{S}$

$B = \dfrac{1}{18,800} = 53.2 \ \mu\text{S}$

$Y = 42 - j53 \ \mu\text{S} = 67 \ \angle{-52°} \ \mu\text{S}$

$Z = \dfrac{1}{67 \ \angle{-52°}} = 15 \ \angle{52°} \ \text{k}\Omega = 9.2 + j12 \ \text{k}\Omega$

(b) $R = 9.2 \ \text{k}\Omega, X_L = 12 \ \text{k}\Omega, \text{and } L = 180 \ \text{mH}$

18. (a) $Y = 150 - j130 \ \mu\text{S} = 200 \ \angle{-42°} \ \mu\text{S}$

$Z = 3.7 + j3.4 \ \text{k}\Omega = 5.0 \ \angle{42°} \ \text{k}\Omega$

(b) $R = 3.7 \ \text{k}\Omega, X_L = 3.4 \ \text{k}\Omega, \text{and } L = 90 \ \text{mH}$

19. (a) $Y = 1.5 + j2.4 \ \text{mS} = 2.8 \ \angle{58°} \ \text{mS}$

$Z = 190 - j310 \ \Omega = 360 \ \angle{-58°} \ \Omega$

(b) $R = 190 \ \Omega, X_C = 310 \ \Omega, \text{and } C = 35 \ \text{pF}$

20. (a) $Y = 1.6 + j1.3 \ \text{mS} = 2.0 \ \angle{38°} \ \text{mS}$

$Z = 390 - j300 \ \Omega = 490 \ \angle{-38°} \ \Omega$

(b) $R = 390 \ \Omega, X_C = 300 \ \text{k}\Omega, \text{and } C = 110 \ \text{nF}$

Exercise 23.4 *RLC* Circuits

1. $I_T = 30 + j(40 - 80) = 30 - j40 \ \text{mA} = 50 \ \angle{-53°} \ \text{mA}$

2. $I_T = 50 - j40 \ \text{mA} = 64 \ \angle{-39°} \ \text{mA}$

3. $I_T = 55 + j60 \ \text{mA} = 81 \ \angle{47°} \ \text{mA}$

4. $I_T = 65 + j30 \ \text{mA} = 72 \ \angle{25°} \ \text{mA}$

5. $I_T = 1.1 - j0.90 \ \text{mA} = 1.4 \ \angle{-39°} \ \text{mA}$

6. $I_T = 500 - j300 \ \mu\text{A} = 580 \ \angle{-31°} \ \mu\text{A}$

7. $I_T = 5.0 + j0 \ \text{mA} = 5.0 \ \angle{0°} \ \text{mA}$

8. $I_T = 12 + j0 \ \text{mA} = 12 \ \angle{0°} \ \text{mA}$

9. $I_T = \dfrac{12}{390} + j\left(\dfrac{12}{750} - \dfrac{12}{430}\right) = 31 - j12 \ \text{mA} = 33 \ \angle{-21°} \ \text{mA}$

$Z_T = \dfrac{12 \ \angle{0°} \ \text{V}}{33 \ \angle{-21°} \ \text{mA}} = 360 \ \angle{21°} \ \Omega = 340 + j130 \ \Omega$

10. $I_T = 21 - j4.0 \ \text{mA} = 22 \ \angle{-11°} \ \text{mA}$

$Z_T = 1.4 + j0.27 \ \text{k}\Omega = 1.5 \ \angle{11°} \ \text{k}\Omega$

11. $I_T = 23 + j14 \ \text{mA} = 26 \ \angle{31°} \ \text{mA}$

$Z_T = 1.2 - j0.71 \ \text{k}\Omega = 1.4 \ \angle{-31°} \ \text{k}\Omega$

12. $I_T = 570 + j220 \ \mu\text{A} = 610 \ \angle{21°} \ \mu\text{A}$

$Z_T = 9.6 - j3.7 \ \text{k}\Omega = 10 \ \angle{-21°} \ \text{k}\Omega$

13. $I_T = 17 - j31 \ \text{mA} = 35 \ \angle{-61°} \ \text{mA}$

$Z_T = 330 + j590 \ \Omega = 680 \ \angle{61°} \ \Omega$

14. $I_T = 6.7 - j2.8$ mA $= 7.3 \angle -23°$ mA

$Z_T = 700 + j290$ Ω $= 760 \angle 23°$ Ω

15. $I_T = 600 + j770$ μA $= 1.0 \angle 52°$ mA

$Z_T = 3.8 - j4.8$ kΩ $= 6.1 \angle -52°$ kΩ

16. $I_T = 6.4 + j0$ mA $= 6.4 \angle 0°$ mA

$Z_T = 2.2 + j0$ kΩ $= 2.2 \angle 0°$ kΩ

17. $Y = \left(\dfrac{1}{390}\right) + j\left(\dfrac{1}{750} - \dfrac{1}{430}\right) = 2.6 - j0.99$ mS

$= 2.7 \angle -21°$ mS

18. $Y = 670 - j120$ μS $= 680 \angle -11°$ μS

19. $Y = 630 + j380$ μS $= 730 \angle 31°$ μS

20. $Y = 91 + j35$ μS $= 98 \angle 21°$ μS

21. $Y = 0.71 - j1.3$ mS $= 1.5 \angle -61°$ mS

22. $Y = 1.2 - j0.52$ mS $= 1.3 \angle -23°$ mS

23. $Y = 100 + j130$ μS $= 160 \angle 52°$ μS

24. $Y = 450 + j0$ μS $= 450 \angle 0°$ μS

25. (a) $X_L = 2\pi(20{,}000)(0.010) = 1257$ Ω

$$X_C = \frac{1}{2\pi(20{,}000)(5.0 \times 10^{-9})} = 1592 \text{ Ω}$$

$$I_T = \frac{10}{4300} + j\left(\frac{10}{1592} - \frac{10}{1257}\right) = 2.3 - j1.7 \text{ mA}$$

$$= 2.9 \angle -36° \text{ mA}$$

$$Z = \frac{10 \angle 0° \text{ V}}{2.9 \angle -36° \text{ mA}} = 3.5 \angle 36° \text{ kΩ}$$

$$= 2.8 + j2.0 \text{ kΩ}$$

(b) $R = 2.8$ kΩ, $X_L = 2.0$ kΩ, and $L = 16$ mH

26. (a) $Y = \dfrac{1}{4300} + j\left(\dfrac{1}{1592} - \dfrac{1}{1257}\right) = 230 - j170$ μS

$= 290 \angle -36°$ μS, $Z = \dfrac{1}{290 \angle -36° \text{ μS}}$

$= 3.5 \angle 36°$ kΩ $= 2.8 + j2.0$ kΩ

(b) $R = 2.8$ kΩ, $X_L = 2.0$ kΩ, and $L = 16$ mH

27. (a) $I_T = 2.2 + 0.77$ mA $= 2.3 \angle 19°$ mA

$Z = 6.1 - j2.1$ kΩ $= 6.4 \angle -19°$ kΩ

(b) $R = 6.1$ kΩ, $X_C = 2.1$ kΩ, and $C = 1.5$ nF

28. (a) $147 + j51$ μS $= 160 \angle 19°$ μS

(b) $R = 6.1$ kΩ, $X_C = 2.1$ kΩ, and $C = 1.5$ nF

29. (a) $R_{eq} = \dfrac{(8.2)(15)}{23.2} = 5.3$ kΩ

$Y = \dfrac{1}{5300} + j\left(\dfrac{1}{10{,}000} - \dfrac{1}{5600}\right) = 190 - j79$ μS

$= 205 \angle -23°$ μS $\rightarrow Z = \dfrac{1}{(205 \angle -23° \text{ μS})}$

$= 4.5 + j1.9$ kΩ

(b) $R = 4.5$ kΩ, $X_L = 1.9$ kΩ, and $L = 25$ mH

30. (a) $Y = 1.5 + j1.6$ mS, $Z = 320 - j330$ Ω

(b) $R = 320$ Ω, $X_C = 330$ Ω, and $C = 480$ nF

31. (a) $Y = 740 \angle -26°$ μS, $Z = 1.3 \angle 26°$ kΩ

(b) $V = 16$ V

32. (a) $Y = 590 \angle 59°$ μS, $Z = 1.7 \angle -59°$ kΩ

(b) $I_T = 15 \angle 59°$ mA

Exercise 23.5 AC Networks

1. $Z_{eq} = \dfrac{(j510)(-j680)}{(j510 - j680)} = \dfrac{-j^2 346{,}800}{-j170} = j2040 \rightarrow Z_T = 1.3 + j2.0$ kΩ $= 2.4 \angle 57°$ kΩ

2. $Z_T = 2.0 - j7.2$ kΩ $= 7.5 \angle -74°$ kΩ

3. $Z_{eq} = \dfrac{(750)(-j820)}{750 - j820} = \dfrac{615{,}000 \angle -90°}{1111 \angle -47.6°} = 554 \angle -42°$ Ω $= 409 - j373 \rightarrow$

$Z_T = X_L + Z_{eq} = j900 + 409 - j373 \approx 410 + j530 = 670 \angle 52°$ Ω

4. $Z_T = 1.4 - j1.3$ kΩ $= 1.9 \angle -41°$ kΩ

5. $X_L = 2\pi(2500)(0.030) = 471\ \Omega$

$X_C = \dfrac{1}{2\pi(2500)(100 \times 10^{-9})} = 637\ \Omega$

$Z_1 \doteq 330 + j471 \rightarrow$

$Z_T = \dfrac{(330 + j471)(-j637)}{330 + j471 - j637} = 990\ \angle{-8.4°}\ \Omega = 980 - j140\ \Omega$

6. $Z_T = 490\ \angle{-59°}\ \Omega = 250 - j420\ \Omega$

7. $Z_{eq} = \dfrac{(5.6)(j4.7)}{5.6 + j4.7} = 3.60\ \angle{50°}\ k\Omega = 2.31 + j2.76\ k\Omega \rightarrow$

$Z_T = X_C + Z_{eq} = 2.3 - j2.3\ k\Omega = 3.3\ \angle{-45°}\ k\Omega$

8. $Z_T = 320 - j370\ \Omega = 490\ \angle{-49°}\ \Omega$

9. $Z_1 = 10 - j20 \rightarrow Z_T = \dfrac{(10 - j20)(j10)}{10 - j20 + j10} = \dfrac{20 + j10}{1 - j} = 5.0 + j15\ k\Omega = 16\ \angle{72°}\ k\Omega$

10. $Z_T = 20 + j10\ k\Omega = 22\ \angle{27°}\ k\Omega$

11. $Z_{eq} = \dfrac{(100 + j500)(200 - j6000)}{100 + j5000 + 200 - j6000} = \dfrac{(5000\ \angle{88.9°})(6000\ \angle{-88.1°})}{1044\ \angle{-73.3°}} = 28.8\ \angle{74.1°}\ k\Omega = 7.88 + j27.7\ k\Omega \rightarrow$

$Z_T = 5.1 + 7.88 + j27.7 \approx 13 + j28\ k\Omega = 31\ \angle{65°}\ k\Omega$

12. $Z_T = 30 - j57\ k\Omega = 65\ \angle{-62°}\ k\Omega$

13. $I_T = \dfrac{V_T}{Z_T} = \dfrac{15.0\ \angle{0°}}{2.45\ \angle{52°}} = 6.1\ \angle{-52°}\ mA = 3.7 - j4.8\ mA$

$V_R = (6.1\ \angle{-52°}\ mA)(1500\ \angle{0°}\ \Omega) = 9.1\ \angle{-52°}\ V = 5.6 - j7.2\ V$

$V_L = V_T - V_R = 15 - (5.6 - j7.2) = 9.4 + j7.2\ V = 12\ \angle{37°}\ V$

14. $I_R = 15\ \angle{-77°}\ mA = 3.5 - j15\ mA,$
$V_R = 2.3\ \angle{-77°}\ V = 0.51 - j2.2\ V,$
$V_L = 9.8\ \angle{13°}\ V = 9.5 + j2.2\ V$

Exercise 23.6 Filters

1. $Z = \sqrt{12^2 + 12^2} = 17\ k\Omega$

$I = \dfrac{20\ V}{17\ k\Omega} = 1.18\ mA$

$V_R = (1.18\ mA)(12\ k\Omega) = 14.1\ V$

$V_C = (1.18\ mA)(12\ k\Omega) = 14.1\ V$

$f_C = \dfrac{1}{2\pi(12\ k\Omega)(10\ nF)} = 1.33\ kHz$

2. $I = 2.83\ mA, V_R = 14.1\ V, V_C = 14.1\ V, f_c = 3.18\ kHz$

3. (a) $f_c = 1.06\ kHz$
   (b) $X_C = 1.5\ k\Omega, I = 4.71\ mA, V_{out} = 7.07\ V$

4. (a) $f_c = 159\ Hz$
   (b) $X_C = 2.0\ k\Omega, I = 3.54\ mA, V_{out} = 7.07\ V$

5. (a) $f_c = 3.18\ kHz$
   (b) $X_L = 1.0\ k\Omega, I = 7.07\ mA, V_{out} = 7.07\ V$

6. (a) $f_c = 1.59\ kHz$
   (b) $X_L = 1.0\ k\Omega, I = 7.07\ mA, V_{out} = 7.07\ V$

7. (a) $f_c = \dfrac{1}{2\pi(1.5\ k\Omega)(10\ nF)} = 10.6\ kHz$

   (b) $X_C = R = 1.5\ k\Omega$

   $Z = \sqrt{1.5^2 + 1.5^2} = 2.12\ k\Omega$

   $I = \dfrac{12\ V}{2.12\ k\Omega} = 5.66\ mA$

   $V_{out} = (5.66\ mA)(1.5\ k\Omega) = 8.49\ V$

8. (a) $f_c = 796\ Hz$
   (b) $X_C = 10\ k\Omega, I = 1.41\ mA, V_{out} = 14.1\ V$

9. (a) $Z = \sqrt{1.0^2 + 2.0^2} = 2.24$ kΩ

$$I = \frac{10}{2.24 \text{ k}\Omega} = 4.47 \text{ mA}$$

$$V_R = (4.47 \text{ mA})(1.0 \text{ k}\Omega) = 4.47 \text{ V}$$

$$V_{\text{out}} = (4.47 \text{ mA})(2.0 \text{ k}\Omega) = 8.94 \text{ V}$$

(b) $f = 3.18$ kHz, $f_c = 1.59$ kHz

10. (a) $I = 5.55$ mA, $V_R = 5.55$ V, $V_{\text{out}} = 8.32$ V

(b) $f = 2.39$ kHz, $f_c = 1.59$ kHz

11. (a) $f_c = 4.77$ kHz

(b) $X_L = 1.5$ kΩ, $I = 9.42$ mA, $V_{\text{out}} = 14.1$ V

12. (a) $f_c = 11.9$ kHz

(b) $X_L = 1.5$ kΩ, $I = 4.71$ mA, $V_{\text{out}} = 7.07$ V

13. $f_{c_2} = \dfrac{1}{2\pi(100)(1.5 \ \mu\text{F})} = 1.06$ kHz

$$f_{c_1} = \dfrac{1}{2\pi(500)(1.0 \ \mu\text{F})} = 318 \text{ Hz}$$

14. $f_{c_2} = 1.59$ kHz, $f_{c_1} = 106$ Hz

Review Exercises

1. $I_T = 2.1 - j1.5$ mA $= 2.5 \ \angle{-35°}$ mA,
$Z = 2.9 + j2.0$ k$\Omega = 3.5 \ \angle{35°}$ kΩ

2. $I_T = 2.7 - j8.3$ mA $= 8.7 \ \angle{-72°}$ mA,
$Z = 0.52 + j1.6$ k$\Omega = 1.7 \ \angle{72°}$ kΩ

3. $I_T = 15 + j6.7$ mA $= 16 \ \angle{24°}$ mA,
$Z = 680 - j310 \ \Omega = 750 \ \angle{-24°}$ Ω

4. $I_T = 4.0 + j9.4$ mA $= 10 \ \angle{67°}$ mA,
$Z = 240 - j580 \ \Omega = 625 \ \angle{-67°}$ Ω

5. $I_T = 3.6 + j2.7$ mA $= 4.5 \ \angle{36°}$ mA,
$Z = 7.2 - j5.2$ k$\Omega = 8.9 \ \angle{-36°}$ kΩ

6. $I_T = 1.5 + j0.50$ mA $= 1.6 \ \angle{18°}$ mA,
$Z = 18 - j6.0$ k$\Omega = 19 \ \angle{-18°}$ kΩ

7. $I_T = 14 - j9.5$ mA $= 17 \ \angle{-34°}$ mA,
$Z = 390 + j260 \ \Omega = 470 \ \angle{34°}$ Ω

8. $I_T = 13 - j8.0$ mA $= 16 \ \angle{-31°}$ mA,
$Z = 1.3 + j0.80$ k$\Omega = 1.5 \ \angle{31°}$ kΩ

9. $I_T = 7.4 + j0.33$ mA $= 7.4 \ \angle{2.6°}$ mA,
$Z = 2.7 - j0.12$ k$\Omega = 2.7 \ \angle{-2.6°}$ kΩ

10. $I_T = 14 + j0$ mA $= 14 \ \angle{0°}$ mA,
$Z = 390 + j0 \ \Omega = 390 \ \angle{0°}$ Ω

11. $B = 160 \ \mu$S, $Y = 230 - j160 \ \mu$S $= 280 \ \angle{-35°} \ \mu$S

12. $B = 560 \ \mu$S, $Y = 180 - j560 \ \mu$S $= 580 \ \angle{-72°} \ \mu$S

13. $B = 560 \ \mu$S, $Y = 1.2 + j0.56$ mS $= 1.3 \ \angle{24°}$ mS

14. $B = 1.5$ mS, $Y = 0.63 + j1.5$ mS $= 1.6 \ \angle{67°}$ mS

15. $B = 67 \ \mu$S, $Y = 91 + j67 \ \mu$S $= 110 \ \angle{36°} \ \mu$S

16. $B = 17 \ \mu$S, $Y = 50 + j17 \ \mu$S $= 53 \ \angle{18°} \ \mu$S

17. $B = 1.2$ mS, $Y = 1.8 - j1.2$ mS $= 2.1 \ \angle{-34°}$ mS

18. $B = 330 \ \mu$S, $Y = 560 - j330 \ \mu$S $= 650 \ \angle{-31°} \ \mu$S

19. $B = 17 \ \mu$S, $Y = 370 + j17 \ \mu$S $= 370 \ \angle{2.6°} \ \mu$S

20. $B = 0.0$ mS, $Y = 2.6 + j0$ mS $= 2.6 \ \angle{0°}$ mS

21. (a) $I_T = 11 - j8.0$ mA $= 13 \ \angle{-37°}$ mA

(b) $Z = 360 + j270 \ \Omega = 450 \ \angle{37°} \ \Omega$;
$R = 360 \ \Omega$, $L = 7.1$ mH

22. (a) $I_T = 10 + j6.3$ mA $= 12 \ \angle{32°}$ mA

(b) $Z = 1.4 - j0.90$ k$\Omega = 1.7 \ \angle{-32°}$ kΩ;
$R = 1.4$ kΩ, $C = 89$ nF

23. (a) $X_L = 2\pi(10{,}000)(0.050) = 3142 \ \Omega$

$$X_L = \frac{1}{2\pi(10{,}000)(10 \times 10^{-9})} = 1592 \ \Omega$$

$$I_T = \frac{24}{1500} + j\left(\frac{24}{1592} - \frac{24}{3142} \right) = 16 + j7.5 \text{ mA}$$

$$= 18 \ \angle{25°} \text{ mA}$$

(b) $Z = \dfrac{24 \text{ V}}{17.6 \ \angle{25°} \text{ mA}} = 1.4 \ \angle{-25°}$ kΩ

$$= 1.2 - j0.57 \text{ k}\Omega$$

$R = 1.2$ kΩ, $X_C = 570 \ \Omega$, and $C = 28$ nF

24. (a) $Y = 1.3 - j2.3$ mS $= 2.7 \ \angle{-60°}$ mS,
$Z = 190 + j320 \ \Omega = 380 \ \angle{60°} \ \Omega$

(b) $V = 17$ V, $R = 190 \ \Omega$, $L = 7.5$ mH

25. (a) $Y = 300 - j590 \ \mu$S $= 660 \ \angle{-63°} \ \mu$S,
$Z = 0.69 + j1.3$ k$\Omega = 1.5 \ \angle{63°}$ kΩ

(b) $R = 690 \ \Omega$, $L = 140$ mH

26. (a) $Y = 0.067 + j1.1$ mS $= 1.1 \ \angle{87°}$ mS,
$Z = 54 - j900 \ \Omega = 900 \ \angle{-87°} \ \Omega$

(b) $R = 54 \ \Omega$, $C = 12$ nF

27. $Z = 1.2 \ \angle{-26°}$ k$\Omega = 1.1 - j0.54$ kΩ

28. $Z = 5.9 \ \angle{39°}$ k$\Omega = 4.6 + j3.7$ kΩ

29. $Z_{eq} = \dfrac{(200 + j2000)(-j1500)}{200 + j500}$

$= \dfrac{(2009 \angle 84.3°)(1500 \angle -90°)}{539 \angle 68.2°}$

$= 5.59 \angle -73.9° \text{ k}\Omega = 1.55 - j5.37 \text{ k}\Omega \rightarrow$

$Z_T = R_1 + Z_{eq} = 2.6 - j5.4 \text{ k}\Omega = 6.0 \angle -65° \text{ k}\Omega$

30. $Z = 3.7 \angle 57° \text{ k}\Omega = 2.1 + j3.1 \text{ k}\Omega$

31. (a) $f_c = 15.9 \text{ kHz}$
    (b) $X_C = 1.0 \text{ k}\Omega$, $I = 14.1 \text{ mA}$, $V_{out} = 14.1 \text{ V}$

32. (a) $I = 4.47 \text{ mA}$, $V_R = 4.47 \text{ V}$, $V_{out} = 8.94 \text{ V}$
    (b) $f = 6.36 \text{ kHz}$, $f_C = 3.18 \text{ kHz}$

CHAPTER 24 Exponents and Logarithms

Exercise 24.1 Fractional Exponents

1. 5

2. 2

3. 16

4. 27

5. 9

6. −729

7. $\frac{1}{8} = 0.125$

8. $\frac{1}{4} = 0.25$

9. $\frac{1}{10} = 0.1$

10. $\frac{1}{100} = 0.01$

11. $\frac{1}{8} = 0.125$

12. 27

13. 0.3

14. 0.4

15. 1.44

16. 2.24

17. 3.16

18. 0.316

19. 100

20. 0.008

21. 125×10^{-3}

22. 1.2×10^3

23. 1.5×10^3

24. 25×10^{-8}

25. $\frac{125}{64} = 1.95$

26. $-\frac{2}{3} = -0.667$

27. 10

28. 2

29. $I_T^{0.4}$

30. $P_1^{0.5}$

31. $-3e^2$

32. $12X_C^2$

33. $\dfrac{5}{L^2 X}$

34. $0.01I^2R^2$

35. $\dfrac{V_x}{10^{-3}}$

36. $\dfrac{10^3}{e}$

37. $72s^3$

38. $-0.8k^2$

39. $\dfrac{2ab^2}{3}$

40. $\dfrac{4}{t}$

41. 8.4 mm

42. 20 min

43. 3.1 kHz

44. 250 mA

45. 0.019

46. $(QR)^{0.6} \left(\dfrac{Q}{R}\right)^{0.4} = Q^{(0.6+0.4)} R^{(0.6-0.4)} = QR^{0.2}$

Exercise 24.2 Exponential Functions

1. $y = 3^x$

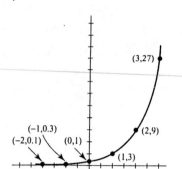

2. $y = 1.5^x$

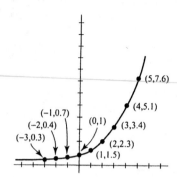

3. $y = 2^{x-1}$

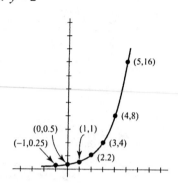

4. $y = 2^{x+1}$

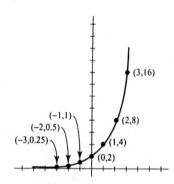

5. $y = 10^{0.2x}$

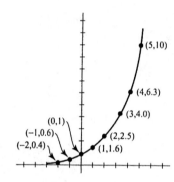

6. $y = 10^{0.3x}$

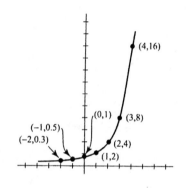

7. $y = 1.5^{-x}$

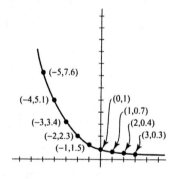

8. $y = 3^{-x}$

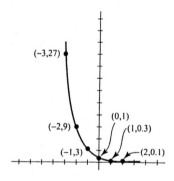

9. $y = 2^{-x+1}$

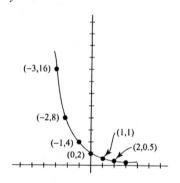

10. $y = 2^{-x-1}$

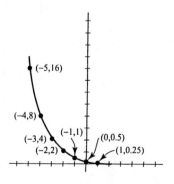

11. $y = 1 - 2^x$

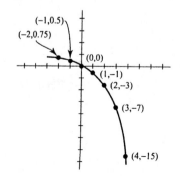

12. $y = 1 - 2^{-x}$

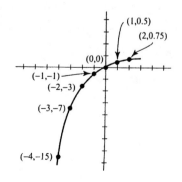

13. $y = e^t$

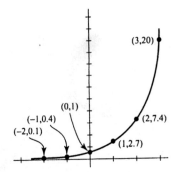

14. $y = 2e^t$

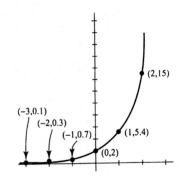

15. $y = 2e^{-t}$

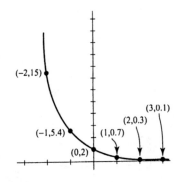

16. $y = e^{-t}$

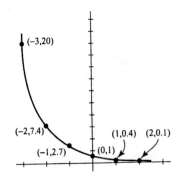

17. $y = 1 - e^{-t}$

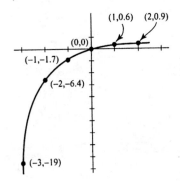

18. $y = 1 - e^t$

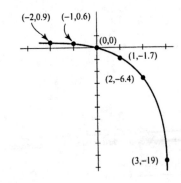

19. $y = 1 - e^{0.5t}$

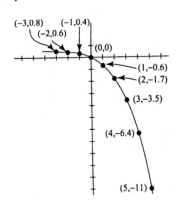

20. $y = 1 - e^{-0.5t}$

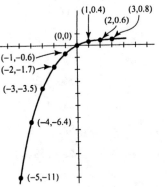

21. (a) $A = 6.0 \times 10^9 (1.015)^n$

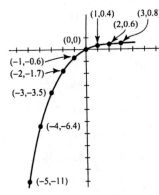

(b) ≈ 2035

22. (a) $p = 10(1.06)^n$

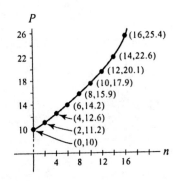

(b) ≈ 12 yrs

23. (a) $\dfrac{-t}{RC} = \dfrac{-0.005}{0.02} = -0.25$

$$v = 25e^{-0.25} = 19.5 \text{ V}$$

(b) 9.2 V

(c) 25 V

24. (a) 20 ms

(b) 4.4 V

(c) 2.7 V

25. (a) $RC = (2.0\ \text{M}\Omega)(200\ \text{nF}) = 400\ \text{ms}$

(b) $i = \dfrac{100}{(2.0 \times 10^6)e^{-0.5}} = 30\ \mu\text{A}$

(c) $18\ \mu\text{A}$

26. (a) $50\ \text{ms}$

(b) $6.3\ \text{V}$

(c) $8.6\ \text{V}$

Exercise 24.3   Common and Natural Logarithms

1. $\log_2 8 = 3$

2. $\log_5 625 = 4$

3. $\log_5 0.2 = -1$

4. $\log_2 0.03125 = -5$

5. $\log 10{,}000 = 4$

6. $\log 39.8 = 1.6$

7. $\log 0.631 = -0.2$

8. $\log 0.01 = -2$

9. $\ln 7.39 = 2$

10. $\ln 1.649 = 0.5$

11. $\ln 0.223 = -1.5$

12. $\ln 0.368 = -1$

13. $\ln 0.100 = -2.3$

14. $\ln 0.535 = -0.625$

15. $5^2 = 25$

16. $2^4 = 16$

17. $2^{-3} = 0.125$

18. $5^{-2} = 0.04$

19. $10^3 = 1000$

20. $10^{2.3} = 200$

21. $10^{-0.5} = 0.316$

22. $10^{-1} = 0.1$

23. $e^{1.1} = 3.0$

24. $e^{4.0} = 54.6$

25. $e^{-1.93} = 0.145$

26. $e^{-0.511} = 0.60$

27. $e^{-2.95} = 0.0523$

28. $e^{-3.55} = 0.0288$

29. 1.94

30. 0.727

31. -0.979

32. -1.32

33. 3.72

34. 6.09

35. -5.59

36. -7.47

37. 3.22

38. 0.358

39. -2.09

40. -0.582

41. -5.03

42. 10.7

43. 209

44. 776×10^3

45. 5.11

46. 2.79

47. 428

48. 5.22×10^3

49. 3.86

50. 7.24

51. 1.47

52. 1.14

53. 759×10^{-6}

54. 0.148

55. 0.259

56. 0.120

57. 0.430

58. 0.547

59. $2 + \log x$

60. $-2 + \log y$

61. $2\log y$

62. $2 + \log ax$

63. t

64. t

65. $\ln e^2 - \ln t = 2 - \ln t$

66. $\ln 5 - t$

67. $\log 10^{2x} - \log 10^{2x} = 0$

68. $\log 5x$

69. $\ln (20e^{-2t})(5e^t) = \ln (100e^{-t})$
$= \ln 100 - \ln e^t = \ln 100 - t$

70. $0.3t$

Review Exercises

1. 9

2. 8

3. 0.01

4. 10

5. −27

6. 4

7. 16×10^{-2}

8. 125×10^6

9. 100

10. e^{-t}

11. $\dfrac{10^6}{I^3}$

12. $\dfrac{0.01r^2}{v^2}$

13. $y = 2^{1.2x}$

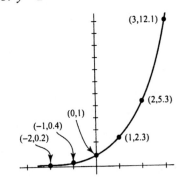

14. $y = 5^{-x/2}$

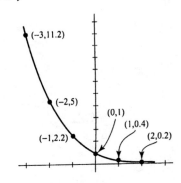

15. $y = e^t - 1$

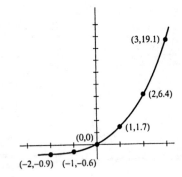

16. $y = 2 - e^{-t}$

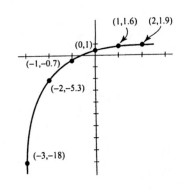

17. $\log 1000 = 3$

18. $\log_2 64 = 6$

19. $\log_5 0.419 = -0.54$

20. $\log 0.00501 = -2.3$

21. $\ln 0.472 = -0.75$

22. $\ln 0.0302 = -3.5$

23. $\ln 54.6 = 4$

24. $\ln 1.32 = 0.28$

25. $10^{-1.11} = 0.0776$

26. $10^{-0.354} = 0.443$

71. **(a)** 23 yrs
(b) 14 yrs
(c) 12 yrs

72. **(a)** 20 s
(b) 54 s

73. $\ln\left(\dfrac{i}{I_0}\right) = -\dfrac{-t}{RC}$

74. $\ln\left(\dfrac{v}{V_0}\right) = -\dfrac{-Rt}{L}$

75. 16 dB

76. $C = \dfrac{(5.8)(0.15)}{(18 \times 10^9)\ \ln\left(\frac{1.1}{1.0}\right)}$
$= 0.51 \text{ nF} = 510 \text{ pF}$

27. $10^{0.727} = 5.33$

28. $10^{1.1} = 12.7$

29. $e^{0.99} = 2.69$

30. $e^{3.14} = 23$

31. $e^{-5.39} = 4.55 \times 10^{-3}$

32. $e^{-0.0284} = 0.972$

33. 1.40

34. 0.826

35. −5.28

36. −0.0306

37. −0.393

38. −3.41

39. 3.60

40. 2.50

41. 7.23

42. 1.08

43. 0.461

44. 562×10^{-6}

45. 67.4

46. 5.00

47. 0.648

48. 4.01×10^{-3}

49. $\log V - 3$

50. $1 + \log q$

51. 0

52. $3 - 2(\ln t)$

53. **(a)** 1.1
(b) 1.1

54. (a) $N = 10(2)^{0.20t}$

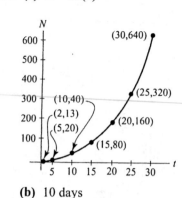

(b) 10 days

55. (a) 1.8 mA
  (b) 400 μA
56. 480 mA
57. (a) $\log V_1 = \log 18 - 1.2$
    $= 0.0553 \rightarrow V_1 = 10^{0.0553}$
  (b) $V_1 = 1.1$ V

58. (a) 2.0
  (b) 53 mA
  (c) 83 mA

CHAPTER 25 Applications of Logarithms

Exercise 25.1 Exponential Equations

1. 4.32

2. 0.379

3. −0.941

4. 2.26

5. 1.30

6. −0.412

7. 0.571

8. −1.01

9. −0.566

10. 0.521

11. 0.330

12. −0.601

13. 1.54

14. −4.11

15. $e^{0.25t} = 2.62 \rightarrow 0.25t$
    $= \ln 2.62 \rightarrow t = 0.00768$

16. 0.924

17. 3.85

18. −0.733

19. 0.0399

20. 0.300

21. (a) $1500 = 1000e^{0.06n} \rightarrow e^{0.06n}$
    $= 1.5 \rightarrow n = 6.8$ yr
  (b) 12 yr
  (c) 18 yr

22. (a) 2010
  (b) 2047

23. (a) 1.4 ms
  (b) 900 μS
24. (a) 6.9 ms
  (b) 12 ms
25. (a) $1 - e^{-0.10t} = \dfrac{12}{13.2} \rightarrow e^{-0.10t}$
      $= 0.091 \rightarrow e = 24$ h
  (b) 35 h
26. (a) $1 - e^{-0.10t} = 0.95 \rightarrow e = 30$ h
  (b) 46 h
27. (a) 1.1 ms
  (b) 8.0 ms
28. (a) 1.8 ms
  (b) 6.7 ms

Exercise 25.2 *RC* and *RL* Circuits

1. 1.0 ms

2. 1.8 ms

3. 2.6 ms

4. 9.2 ms

5. 4.0 ms

6. 3.3 ms

7. 540 μs

8. 640 μs

9. 2.0 ms

10. 1.6 ms

11. 6.7 ms

12. 6.4 ms

13. 750 μs

14. 770 μs

15. 210 μs

16. 300 μs

17. (a) 2.0 ms

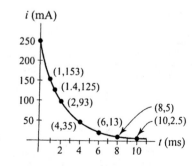

(b) $i = 250e^{-t/2}$

18. (a) 10 ms

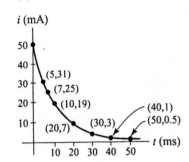

(b) $i = 50e^{-t/10}$

19. (a) 4.0 ms

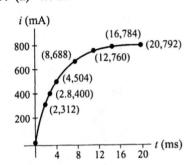

(b) $i = 800(1 - e^{-t/4})$

20. (a) 800 μs

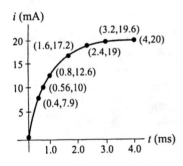

(b) $i = 20(1 - e^{-t/0.80})$

21. (a) $\tau = RC = (750)(20 \times 10^{-6}) = 15$ ms $\rightarrow$

$$i_C = \left(\frac{60}{750}\right)e^{-0.020/0.015} = 21 \text{ mA}$$

$$v_C = 60(1 - e^{-0.020/0.015}) = 44 \text{ V}$$

(b) $0.050 = 0.08e^{-t/0.015} \rightarrow t = \dfrac{\ln 0.625}{-66.7} = 7.1$ ms

(c) $25 = 60(1 - e^{-66.7t}) \rightarrow t = \dfrac{\ln 0.583}{66.7} = 8.1$ ms

22. (a) 41 mA, 31 V

(b) 31 ms

(c) 27 ms

23. (a) From Table 25-1: $t = 0.70\tau = 10$ ms

(b) $1 - e^{-66.7t} = 0.90 \rightarrow t = \dfrac{\ln 0.10}{-66.7} = 35$ ms

24. (a) 14 ms

(b) 3.3 ms

25. (a) 910 mA

(b) 3.5 ms

(c) 1.2 ms

26. (a) 450 mA

(b) 6.9 ms

(c) 15 ms

27. (a) 570 μC

(b) 9.4 ms

(c) 60 ms

28. (a) 12 V

(b) 290 μS

(c) 1.0 ms

Exercise 25.3   Power and Gain

1. 20 dB

2. 22 dB

3. 25 dB

4. 32 dB

5. 19 dB

6. 18 dB

7. 34 dB

8. 32 dB

9. 40 dB

10. 38 dB

11. 48 dB

12. 56 dB

13. 33 dB

14. 34 dB

15. 32 dB

16. 35 dB

17. 39 dB

18. 29 dB

19. 30 dB

20. 24 dB

21. 12 dB

22. 20 dB

23. 9.5 dB

24. 8.5 dB

25. 16 dB

26. 16 dB

27. $10 \log\left(\dfrac{P_{out}}{0.007}\right) = 30 \rightarrow$

$\dfrac{P_{out}}{0.007} = 10^3$

$= 10^3 \rightarrow P_{out} = 7.0 \text{ W}$

28. 3.2 W

29. 100 mW

30. 6.0 W

31. 160 mW

32. 13 mW

33. 63 mW

34. 320 mW

35. 8.4 V

36. 2.5 V

37. 980 mV

38. 63 mV

39. 380 mV

40. 200 mV

41. 84 mV

42. 130 mV

43. $10 \log\left(\dfrac{2.0}{1.0}\right) = 3.0 \text{ dB}$

44. 5.2 dB

45. 8.2 dB

46. 7.8 dB

Review Exercises

1. 5.21

2. 0.492

3. 1.09

4. −0.522

5. 0.0693

6. 0.183

7. 1.4 ms

8. 6.7 ms

9. 4.0 ms

10. 1.4 ms

11. 12 ms

12. 7.8 ms

13. 530 µs

14. 630 µs

15. 22 dB

16. 32 dB

17. 18 dB

18. 33 dB

19. 46 dB

20. 20 dB

21. 88 dB

22. 69 dB

23. 2.5 W

24. 80 W

25. 5.0 W

26. 10 mW

27. 32 V

28. 63 mV

29. 2.8 V

30. 230 mV

31. **(a)** $\tau = (1500)(10 \times 10^{-6}) = 15 \text{ ms}$

   (b) $i_C = \dfrac{40}{1.5e^{-t/0.015}} = 27e^{-67t}$

   (c) $v_C = 40(1 - e^{-67t})$

   (d) 14 mA, 20 V

   (e) 25 ms

   (f) 10 ms

32. **(a)** $i_C = 27e^{-67t}$

   (b) $v_C = 40e^{-67t}$

   (c) 18 mA, 27 V

   (d) 12 ms

   (e) 4.3 ms

33. **(a)** From Table 25-1:
   $t = 0.50\tau = 0.50(15 \text{ ms}) = 7.5 \text{ ms}$

   (b) $1 - e^{-67t} = 0.80 \rightarrow t = 24 \text{ ms}$

34. **(a)** 15 ms

   (b) 18 ms

35. **(a)** 5 ms

   (b) $i_L = 1.0(1 - e^{-200t})$

   (c) 800 mA

   (d) 5.2 ms

   (e) 15 ms

36. **(a)** $i_L = 1.0e^{-200t}$

   (b) 91 mA

   (c) 6.0 ms

   (d) 3.5 ms

37. **(a)** $v_R = 9.0e^{-83t}$

   (b) 1.7 V

   (c) 6.1 ms

38. **(a)** $v_R = 60(1 - e^{-250t})$

   (b) 16 V

   (c) 16 ms

39. 2.0 W, 47 V

40. 7.0 dB

CHAPTER 26 Boolean Algebra

Exercise 26.1 Boolean Algebra

1. Copper is a poor conductor and $(0.1)^2 = 0.01$. Not True.
   Copper is a poor conductor or $(0.1)^2 = 0.01$. True.
   Copper is not a poor conductor. True.
   $(0.1)^2 \neq 0.01$. Not True.

2. $V = IR$ and New York is in California. Not True.
   $V = IR$ or New York is in California. True.
   $V \neq IR$. Not True.
   New York is not in California. True.

3. Commutative laws, Identity laws, and the Distributive law: $A(B + C) = AB + AC$

4. For addition, if $x + (-x) = 0$, then $x(-x) \neq 1$.
   For multiplication, if $x(\frac{1}{x}) = 1$, then $x + (\frac{1}{x}) \neq 0$.

5. $AB = BA$

6. $(AB)C = A(BC)$

7. $A + 0 = A$

8. $A + \overline{A} = 1$

9. $A \cdot 0 = 0$

10. $A \cdot \overline{A} = 0$

11. $A \cdot 0 = A \cdot \overline{A}$

12. $A \cdot 1 = A + A$

13. $A + (B \cdot 0) = A \cdot 1$

14. $(A + B)(B + C) = AC + B$

15. $A(\overline{A} + B) = AB$

16. $\overline{AB} = \overline{A} + \overline{B}$

17.

A	A + A
1	1
0	0

18.

A	AA	$\overline{A}$	$\overline{AA}$
1	1	0	0
0	0	1	1

19.

A	B	A + B	A(A + B)
0	0	0	0
0	1	1	0
1	0	1	1
1	1	1	1

20.

A	B	A + B	(A + B)(A + B)
0	0	0	0
0	1	1	1
1	0	1	1
1	1	1	1

21.

A	B	AB	$\overline{\overline{AB}}$
0	0	0	0
0	1	0	0
1	0	0	0
1	1	1	1

22.

A	B	$\overline{A}$	$\overline{A}B$	A + B	$A + \overline{A}B$
0	0	1	0	0	0
0	1	1	1	1	1
1	0	0	0	1	1
1	1	0	0	1	1

23.

A	B	$\overline{A}$	$\overline{B}$	$\overline{A}\,\overline{B}$	$\overline{A} + \overline{A}\,\overline{B}$
0	0	1	1	1	1
0	1	1	0	0	1
1	0	0	1	0	0
1	1	0	0	0	0

24.

A	B	$\overline{A}$	$\overline{B}$	$\overline{A}\,\overline{B}$	A + B	$\overline{A + B}$
0	0	1	1	1	0	1
0	1	1	0	0	1	0
1	0	0	1	0	1	0
1	1	0	0	0	1	0

25.

A	B	C	A + B	B + C	(A + B) + C	A + (B + C)
0	0	0	0	0	0	0
0	0	1	0	1	1	1
0	1	0	1	1	1	1
0	1	1	1	1	1	1
1	0	0	1	0	1	1
1	0	1	1	1	1	1
1	1	0	1	1	1	1
1	1	1	1	1	1	1

26.

A	B	C	A + B	A + C	(A + B)(A + C)	BC	A + BC
0	0	0	0	0	0	0	0
0	0	1	0	1	0	0	0
0	1	0	1	0	0	0	0
0	1	1	1	1	1	1	1
1	0	0	1	1	1	0	1
1	0	1	1	1	1	0	1
1	1	0	1	1	1	0	1
1	1	1	1	1	1	1	1

28.

A	B	C	$\overline{A}$	$\overline{B}$	$\overline{C}$	ABC	$\overline{A} + \overline{B} + \overline{C}$	$\overline{ABC}$
0	0	0	1	1	1	0	1	1
0	0	1	1	1	0	0	1	1
0	1	0	1	0	1	0	1	1
0	1	1	1	0	0	0	1	1
1	0	0	0	1	1	0	1	1
1	0	1	0	1	0	0	1	1
1	1	0	0	0	1	0	1	1
1	1	1	0	0	0	1	0	0

27.

A	B	C	$\overline{A}$	$\overline{B}$	$\overline{C}$	$\overline{B}\,\overline{C}$	$\overline{B + C}$	$\overline{A}(\overline{B}\,\overline{C})$	$\overline{A}(\overline{B + C})$
0	0	0	1	1	1	1	1	1	1
0	0	1	1	1	0	0	0	0	0
0	1	0	1	0	1	0	0	0	0
0	1	1	1	0	0	0	0	0	0
1	0	0	0	1	1	1	1	0	0
1	0	1	0	1	0	0	0	0	0
1	1	0	0	0	1	0	0	0	0
1	1	1	0	0	0	0	0	0	0

29. $A(A + B) = AA + AB = A + AB = A(1 + B) = A(1) = A$

30. $B(A + AB) = BA(1 + B) = BA(1) = BA = AB$

Exercise 26.2   Logic Circuits

1. (a) $(A$ and $B)$ or C
   (b) C and $(A$ or $B)$

2. $A \cdot B + C$

3. 0
4. 1
5. 0
6. 0
7. 0
8. 1
9. 1
10. 1
11. 0
12. 1
13. 1
14. 0
15. 1

16. 1
17. 0
18. 1
19. 0
20. 0
21. 0
22. 1
23. 1
24. 0
25. (a) $A + A\overline{B}$

(b)

A	B	$\overline{B}$	$A\overline{B}$	$A + A\overline{B}$
0	0	1	0	0
0	1	0	0	0
1	0	1	1	1
1	1	0	0	1

26. (a) $\overline{A} + \overline{A}B$

(b)

A	B	$\overline{A}$	$\overline{A}B$	$\overline{A} + \overline{A}B$
0	0	1	0	1
0	1	1	1	1
1	0	0	0	0
1	1	0	0	0

27. (a) $AB + \overline{A}B$

(b)

A	B	$\overline{A}$	AB	$\overline{A}B$	$AB + \overline{A}B$
0	0	1	0	0	0
0	1	1	0	1	1
1	0	0	0	0	0
1	1	0	1	0	1

28. (a) $A + AB + AB$

(b)

A	B	AB	$A + AB$	$A + AB + AB$
0	0	0	0	0
0	1	0	0	0
1	0	0	1	1
1	1	1	1	1

29. $A + A\overline{B} = A(1 + \overline{B}) = A(1) = A$

30. $\overline{A} + \overline{A}B = \overline{A}(1 + B) = \overline{A}(1) = \overline{A}$

31. $AB + \overline{A}B = B(A + \overline{A}) = B(1) = B$

32. $A + AB + AB = A + AB = A(1 + B) = A(1) = A$

33. (a) $\overline{AB} + \overline{AB}$

(b)

A	B	$\overline{AB}$	$\overline{AB} + \overline{AB}$
0	0	1	1
0	1	1	1
1	0	1	1
1	1	0	0

(c) $\overline{AB} + \overline{AB} = \overline{AB}$

34. (a) $\overline{(A + B)(\overline{A} + B)}$

(b)

A	B	$\overline{A} + B$	$\overline{(A + B)(\overline{A} + B)}$	$A + B$
0	0	1	0	0
0	1	0	1	1
1	0	0	1	1
1	1	0	1	1

(c) $\overline{(A + B)(\overline{A} + B)} = \overline{(\overline{A + B})} = A + B$

35. (a) $ABC + \overline{A}BC$

(b)

A	B	C	$\overline{A}$	BC	ABC	$\overline{A}BC$	$ABC + \overline{A}BC$
0	0	0	1	0	0	0	0
0	0	1	1	0	0	0	0
0	1	0	1	0	0	0	0
0	1	1	1	1	0	1	1
1	0	0	0	0	0	0	0
1	0	1	0	0	0	0	0
1	1	0	0	0	0	0	0
1	1	1	0	1	1	0	1

(c) $ABC + \overline{A}BC = BC(A + \overline{A}) = BC(1) = BC$

36. (a) $A\overline{BC} + ABC$

(b)

A	B	C	BC	$\overline{BC}$	$A\overline{BC}$	ABC	$A\overline{BC} + ABC$
0	0	0	0	1	0	0	0
0	0	1	0	1	0	0	0
0	1	0	0	1	0	0	0
0	1	1	1	0	0	0	0
1	0	0	0	1	1	0	1
1	0	1	0	1	1	0	1
1	1	0	0	1	1	0	1
1	1	1	1	0	0	1	1

(c) $A\overline{BC} + ABC = A(\overline{BC} + BC) = A(1) = A$

Exercise 26.3 Karnaugh Maps

1. B

2. $\overline{B}$

3. $\overline{A}$

4. A

5. $\overline{A} + \overline{B}$

6. $A + B$

7. $\overline{A} + B$

8. $A + \overline{B}$

9. $AB + BC$

10. $\overline{A}B + \overline{A}\,C$

11. $\overline{A}\,\overline{B} + \overline{B}C$

12. $A\overline{C} + \overline{B}\,\overline{C}$

13. $\overline{B}\,\overline{C} + \overline{A}BC$

14. $\overline{A}\,\overline{B} + ABC$

15. Four adjacent squares $= A$

16. Four adjacent squares $= \overline{A}$

17. No adjacent squares

18. No adjacent squares

19. One row $= \overline{C}\,\overline{D}$

20. One row $= AD$

21. Two sets of 2 adjacent squares $= \overline{A}\,\overline{B}C + \overline{B}CD$

22. Two sets of 2 adjacent squares $= AB\overline{D} + AC\overline{D}$

23. $AB + A\overline{B}(C + \overline{C}) = AB + A\overline{B}(1) = A(B + \overline{B}) = A$

24. $\overline{A}BC + ABC(D + \overline{D}) = \overline{A}BC + ABC = BC(\overline{A} + A) = BC$

Review Exercises

1. (a)

A	B	AB	A + AB
0	0	0	0
0	1	0	0
1	0	0	1
1	1	1	1

(b) $A + AB = A(1 + B) = A(1) = A$

(c) $A(A + B) = A$

2. (a)

A	B	C	BC	A + BC	A(A + BC)
0	0	0	0	0	0
0	0	1	0	0	0
0	1	0	0	0	0
0	1	1	1	1	0
1	0	0	0	1	1
1	0	1	0	1	1
1	1	0	0	1	1
1	1	1	1	1	1

(b) $A(A + BC) = AA + ABC = A + ABC = A(1 + BC)$
$= A(1) = A$

(c) $A + A(B + C) = A$

3. (a)

A	B	$\overline{A}$	$\overline{B}$	$\overline{A}B$	$A\overline{B}$	$\overline{A}B + A\overline{B}$
0	0	1	1	0	1	1
0	1	1	0	1	0	1
1	0	0	1	0	0	0
1	1	0	0	0	0	0

(b) $\overline{A}B + \overline{A}\,\overline{B} = \overline{A}(B + \overline{B}) = \overline{A}(1) = \overline{A}$

(c) $(\overline{A} + B)(\overline{A} + \overline{B}) = \overline{A}$

4. (a)

A	B	$\overline{A}$	$\overline{A} + B$	$A(\overline{A} + B)$	AB
0	0	1	1	0	0
0	1	1	1	0	0
1	0	0	0	0	0
1	1	0	1	1	1

(b) $A(\overline{A} + B) = A\overline{A} + AB = 0 + AB = AB$

(c) $A + \overline{A}B = A + B$

5. (a)

A	B	C	A + B	B + C	AC	AC + B	(A + B)(B + C)
0	0	0	0	0	0	0	0
0	0	1	0	1	0	0	0
0	1	0	1	1	0	1	1
0	1	1	1	1	0	1	1
1	0	0	1	0	0	0	0
1	0	1	1	1	1	1	1
1	1	0	1	1	0	1	1
1	1	1	1	1	1	1	1

(b) $(A + B)(B + C) = AB + AC + BB + BC = AB + AC$
$+ B + BC = AB + AC + B(1 + C) = AB + AC + B$
$= AC + B(1 + A) = AC + B$

(c) $AB + BC = (A + C)B$

6. (a)

A	B	C	$\overline{A}$	B + C	$\overline{B + C}$	$\overline{A}(B + C)$	$\overline{A}\,\overline{B}\,\overline{C}$
0	0	0	1	0	1	1	1
0	0	1	1	1	0	0	0
0	1	0	1	1	0	0	0
0	1	1	1	1	0	0	0
1	0	0	0	0	1	0	0
1	0	1	0	1	0	0	0
1	1	0	0	1	0	0	0
1	1	1	0	1	0	0	0

(b) $\overline{A(B + C)} = \overline{A}(\overline{B} \cdot \overline{C}) = \overline{A} \cdot \overline{B} \cdot \overline{C}$

(c) $\overline{A + BC} = \overline{A} + \overline{B} + \overline{C}$

7. 0

8. 1

9. 0

10. 1

11. 0

12. 1

13. (a) $(A + B)(A + B) = A + B$

(b)

A	B	A + B	(A + B)(A + B)
0	0	0	0
0	1	1	1
1	0	1	1
1	1	1	1

(c) $(A + B)(A + B) = A + B$

14. (a) $A + \overline{A}B = A + B$

(b)

A	B	$\overline{A}$	$\overline{A}B$	$A + \overline{A}B$	A + B
0	0	1	0	0	0
0	1	1	1	1	1
1	0	0	0	1	1
1	1	0	0	1	1

(c) $A + \overline{A}B = A(1 + B) + \overline{A}B = A + AB + \overline{A}B$
$= A + B(A + \overline{A}) = A + B(1) = A + B$

15. (a) $AB + ABC$

(b)

A	B	C	AB	ABC	AB + ABC
0	0	0	0	0	0
0	0	1	0	0	0
0	1	0	0	0	0
0	1	1	0	0	0
1	0	0	0	0	0
1	0	1	0	0	0
1	1	0	1	0	1
1	1	1	1	1	1

(c) $AB + ABC = AB(1 + C) = AB(1) = AB$

16. (a) $\overline{A + B} + \overline{A}B$

(b)

A	B	A + B	$\overline{A + B}$	AB	$\overline{AB}$	$\overline{A + B} + \overline{A}B$	$\overline{A} + \overline{B}$
0	0	0	1	0	1	1	1
0	1	1	0	0	1	1	1
1	0	1	0	0	1	1	1
1	1	1	0	1	0	0	0

(c) $\overline{A + B} + \overline{A}B = \overline{A} \cdot \overline{B} + \overline{A} + \overline{B} = \overline{A}(\overline{B} + 1) + \overline{B} = \overline{A} + \overline{B}$

17. 1

18. AB

19. $\overline{A}\,\overline{B} + \overline{A}\,\overline{C}$

20. $AC + \overline{B}C$

21. Four adjacent squares $= B$

22. Two sets of 2 adjacent squares $= ABC + AB\overline{D}$

CHAPTER 27 Statistics

Exercise 27.1 Mean, Median, and Mode

1. $\overline{x} = 7.73$, Median = 7, Mode = 7

2. $\overline{x} = 73.3$, Median = 75, Mode = 82

3. $\overline{x} = 6.79$, Median = 6.2, No mode

4. $\overline{x} = 2.99$, Median = 3.3, Modes = 3.3, 4.1

5. $\overline{x} = 104$, Median = 104.5, Mode = 105

6. $\overline{x} = 133.6$, Median = 133.5, Modes = 132, 133, 134

7. (a) $\overline{x} = 17.73$, Median = 17, Mode = 17
(b) Mean, median and mode increase by same amount

8. (a) $\overline{x} = 77.3$, Median = 70, Modes = 70
(b) Mean, median and mode are multiplied by same amount

9. (a) Mean = median = 3
(b) X: Terms do not vary;
Y: Terms increase uniformly

10. (a) mean = median = 23.5
(b) Terms vary more in second

11. (a) 2.875
(b) B

12. (a) 2.67
(b) B

13. $\overline{x} = 79.7$, Median = 80, Mode = 80

14. $\overline{x} = 16.2$, Median = 17, Mode = 20

15. (a) $\bar{x} = 7.92\%$, Median = 7.85%, Mode = 7.85%

    (b) Mean best represents the average rate

16. (a) $\bar{x} = \$44{,}917$, Median = $32,500, No mode

    (b) Median best represents the average salary

17. (a) $\bar{x} = 9.11$ V, Median = 9.1 V, Mode = 9.1 V

x(V)	f
8.9	2
9.0	3
9.1	6
9.2	2
9.3	2
9.4	1

    (b) Mean best represents actual voltage

18. (a) $\bar{x} = 1231$ kW, Median = 1200 kW,
Mode = 1200 kW

x(kW)	f
1000	2
1100	3
1200	4
1300	3
1400	3
1500	1

    (b) Mean best represents average power output

19. (a) $\bar{x} = 27.4$ mH, Median = 27.4 mH, Mode = 27.4 mH

x(mH)	f
27.2	2
27.3	5
27.4	6
27.5	4
27.6	1

    (b) All equally represent the inductance

20. (a) $\bar{x} = 1504$ Ω, Median = 1500 Ω,
Modes = 1500 Ω, 1510 Ω

x(Ω)	f
1490	4
1500	7
1510	7
1520	3

    (b) Median best represents the impedance

Exercise 27.2   Standard Deviation

1. $\bar{x} = 5.17$, $\sigma_{n-1} = 3.31$

2. $\bar{x} = 6.17$, $\sigma_{n-1} = 3.19$

3. $\bar{x} = 36.1$, $\sigma_{n-1} = 8.07$

4. $\bar{x} = 23.1$, $\sigma_{n-1} = 7.31$

5. $\bar{x} = 5.48$, $\sigma_{n-1} = 0.299$

6. $\bar{x} = 1.77$, $\sigma_{n-1} = 0.224$

7. $\bar{x} = 105$, $\sigma_{n-1} = 3.46$

8. $\bar{x} = 161$, $\sigma_{n-1} = 6.80$

9. (a) $\bar{x} = 15.17$, $\sigma_{n-1} = 3.31$

    (b) Mean is increased by the same amount; standard deviation does not change.

10. (a) $\bar{x} = 61.7$, $\sigma_{n-1} = 31.9$

    (b) Mean and standard deviation are both multiplied by the same amount.

11. $\bar{x} = 7.53$, $\sigma_{n-1} = 1.60$

x	f
5	2
6	2
7	3
8	4
9	2
10	2

12. $\bar{x} = 4.93$, $\sigma_{n-1} = 2.22$

x	f
1	1
3	4
4	1
5	3
6	3
7	2
10	1

13. $\bar{x} = 1.29, \sigma_{n-1} = 0.144$

x	f
1.1	3
1.2	4
1.3	3
1.4	3
1.5	3

14. $\bar{x} = 2.39, \sigma_{n-1} = 0.203$

x	f
2.1	2
2.2	3
2.3	2
2.4	3
2.5	2
2.6	3
2.8	1

15. $\bar{x} = 15.8, \sigma_{n-1} = 3.94$

16. $\bar{x} = 27.1, \sigma_{n-1} = 1.38$

17. $\bar{x} = \$3180, \sigma_{n-1} = \$455$

18. $\bar{x} = 3.85\%, \sigma_{n-1} = 0.0779\%$

19. $\bar{x} = 40.6 \text{ mA}, \sigma_{n-1} = 1.06 \text{ mA}$

20. $\bar{x} = 100.4 \ \Omega, \sigma_{n-1} = 1.51 \ \Omega$

21. (a)

x(V)	f
1.4	3
1.5	8
1.6	5
1.7	4
1.8	1

(b) $\bar{x} = 1.56 \text{ V}, \sigma_{n-1} = 0.112 \text{ V}$

22. (a)

x(Ω)	f
1.2	3
1.3	4
1.4	6
1.5	3

(b) $\bar{x} = 1.36 \text{ k}\Omega, \sigma_{n-1} = 0.103 \text{ k}\Omega$

Exercise 27.3   **Histograms and the Normal Curve**

1.

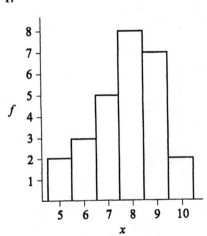

2.

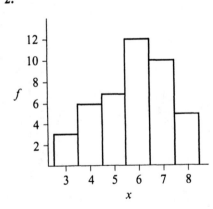

3.

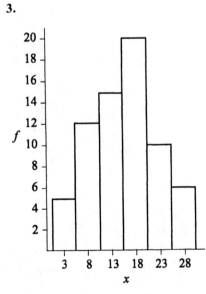

4.

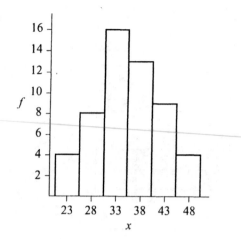

5.

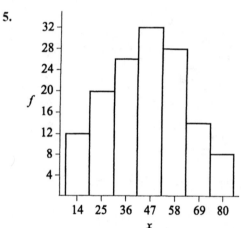

6.

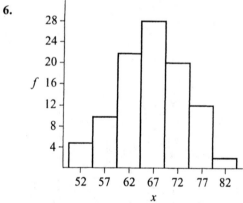

7. (a) 50%

(b) Within two σ of the mean = 68%

(c) Within two σ of the mean = 95%

(d) Outside two σ of the mean = 100% − 95% = 5%

8. (a) 50%

(b) 68%

(c) 99.7%

(d) 0.3%

9.

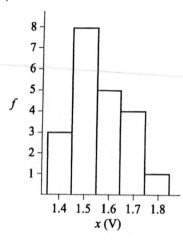

10.

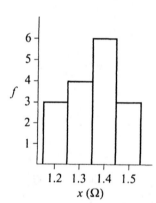

11.

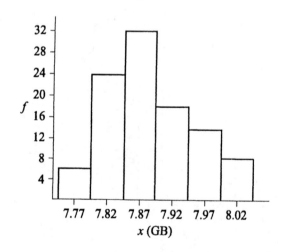

12.

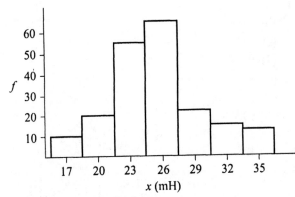

13. (a) 50%

(b) Within one σ of the mean = 68%

(c) Within three σ of the mean = 99.7%

(d) Outside one σ of the mean = 100% − 68% = 32%

Review Exercises

1. $\bar{x} = 12$, Median = 13, No Mode, $\sigma_{n-1} = 7.75$

2. $\bar{x} = 24.4$, Median = 17, Mode = 17, $\sigma_{n-1} = 18.6$

3. $\bar{x} = 1.43$, Median = 1.5, Mode = 1.5, $\sigma_{n-1} = 0.30$

4. $\bar{x} = 204$, Median = 203.5, Mode = 200, $\sigma_{n-1} = 3.59$

5.

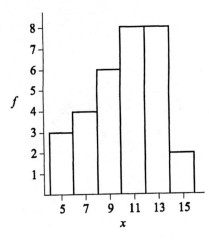

6.

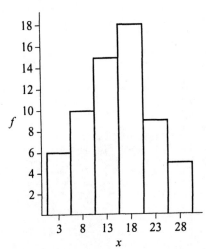

14. (a) 50%

(b) 68%

(c) 95%

(d) 5%

15. (a) Percentage between the mean and one σ below the mean = (68%)/2 = 34%

(b) 50% − 34% = 16%

(c) 50% + 34% = 84%

16. (a) 47.5%

(b) 97.5%

(c) 2.5%

7. (a) $\bar{x} = 50.2$ ft, Median = 50 ft, Mode = 50 ft

(b) $\sigma_{n-1} = 1.32$ ft

8. (a)

Grade	f
0.0	1
1.0	3
2.0	7
3.0	3
4.0	2

(b) $\bar{x} = 2.13$, $\sigma_{n-1} = 1.09$

(c)

9. (a) $\bar{x} = 1.11$ mH, Median = 1.11 mH, Mode = 1.12 mH

(b) $\sigma_{n-1} = 0.0113$ mH

10. (a)

x(W)	f
97	2
98	2
99	4
100	3
101	3
102	1
103	3

(b) $\bar{x} = 100$ W, $\sigma_{n-1} = 1.94$ W

(c)

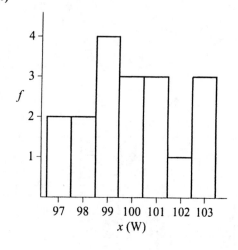

11. (a) 50%
  (b) 68%
  (c) 95%
  (d) 0.3%

12. (a) 50%
  (b) 68%
  (c) 99.7%
  (d) 5%